11+ Non-verbal Reasoning

Year 4/5

Testpack A

(GL Assessment Style)

Practice Paper 1

W0007288

GW0073zzz0

Please read the following before you start the Practice Paper:

1. Do not begin the Practice Paper until you are told to do so.

2. The Practice Paper contains 48 questions and you have 40 minutes to complete it.

3. Read the questions carefully so that you know what to do.

4. Try and answer as many questions as you can. Do not spend too much time on one question. If you cannot answer a question go on to the next one. If a question is omitted, ensure you have marked it clearly on your question paper, so it is easy to find it when you want to return to it after completing the rest of the paper.

5. If you are doing the Practice Paper as a standard test, circle your answer. If you want to change an answer, put a single line through the wrong answer and write the correct answer clearly.

   If you are doing the Practice Paper as a multiple-choice test, draw a clear line through your chosen box. If you want to change an answer, rub it out and mark the correct box clearly. **Do not write on or mark the answer sheet in any way other than that which has been specified.**

6. If you finish before your time ends, go back and check your answers.

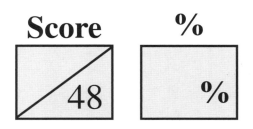

Section 1

In each of the rows below there are five figures. Find one figure in each row that is **most unlike** the other four.

Example

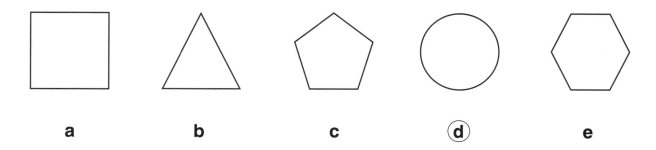

| a | b | c | d | e |

Now do the questions below. Circle the correct answer.

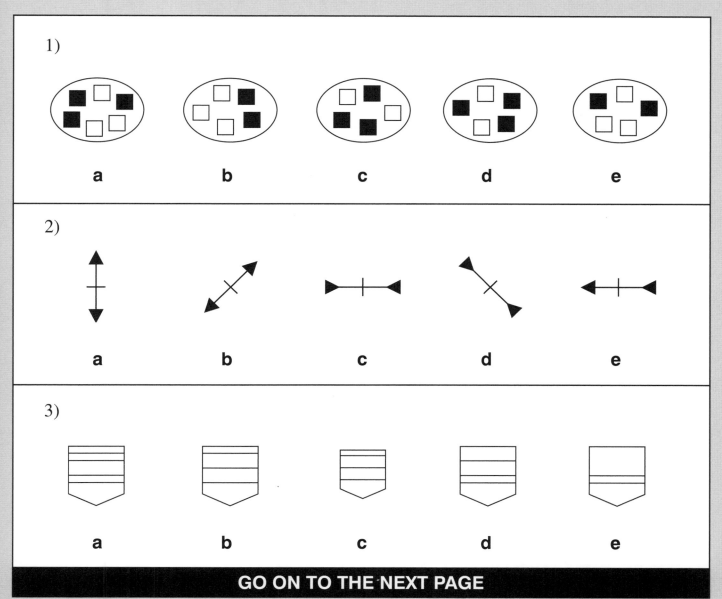

1)

| a | b | c | d | e |

2)

| a | b | c | d | e |

3)

| a | b | c | d | e |

GO ON TO THE NEXT PAGE

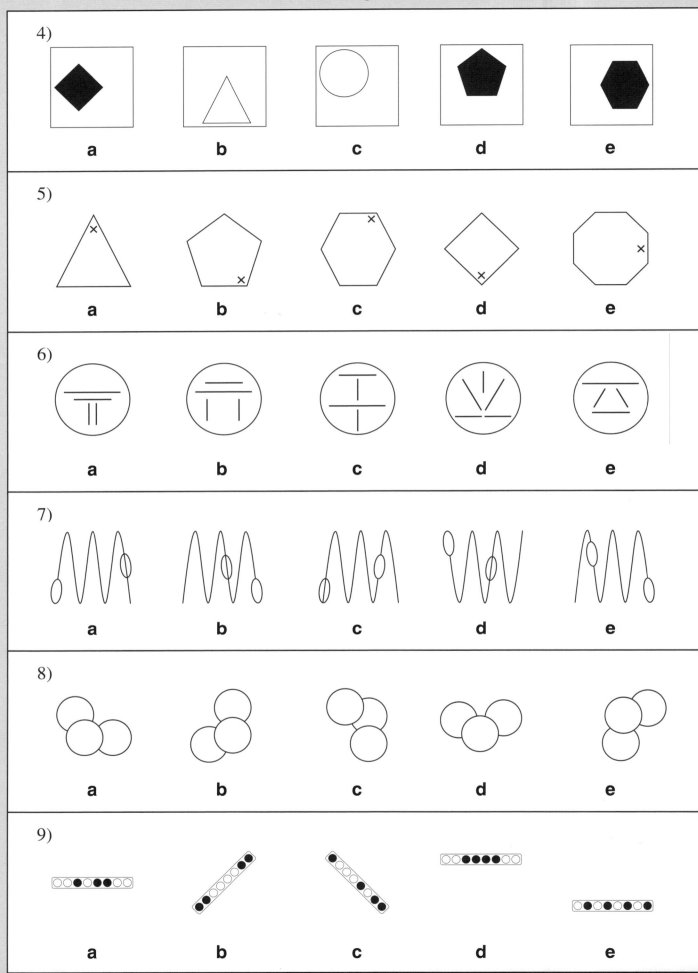

4)

    a   b   c   d   e

5)

    a   b   c   d   e

6)

    a   b   c   d   e

7)

    a   b   c   d   e

8)

    a   b   c   d   e

9)

    a   b   c   d   e

GO ON TO THE NEXT PAGE

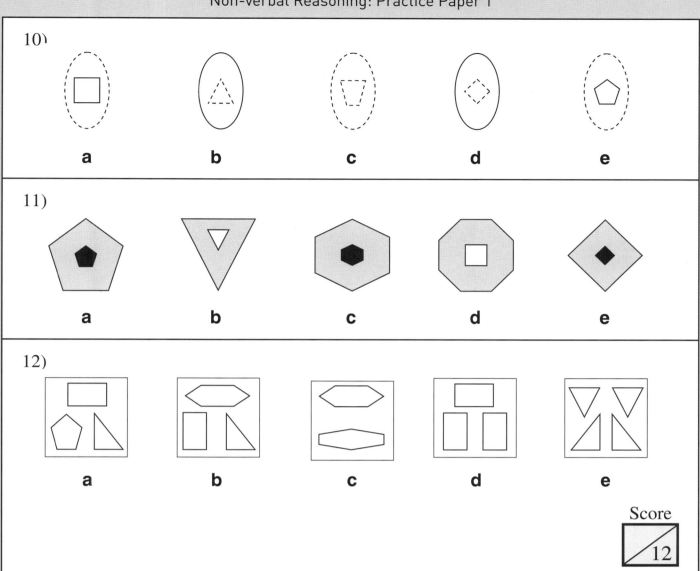

10)

     a   **b**   **c**   **d**   **e**

11)

     a   **b**   **c**   **d**   **e**

12)

     a   **b**   **c**   **d**   **e**

Score

/12

GO ON TO THE NEXT PAGE

Section 2

The following shapes correspond to the codes below them. You must decide how the code letters go with the shapes and then find the correct code for the Test Shape.

Example

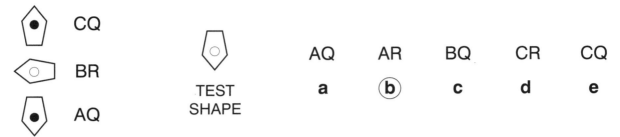

In this example each shape has two code letters. The first letter of each code refers to one aspect of the shape. Each shape has a different letter **A**, **B**, and **C**. What is different about each of the shapes? They are each turned in a different direction. The Test Shape points in the same direction as **A**, so its code letter must be **A**.

The second code letter refers to another aspect of the shape. Two of the shapes have the code **Q**. What is the same in the shapes? They both have black circles, whereas the shape with the code **R** has a white circle. The Test Shape has a white circle, and therefore the second code letter must be **R**.

Now we can tell that the code for the Test Shape shape must be **AR**.

Now do the questions below. Circle the correct answer.

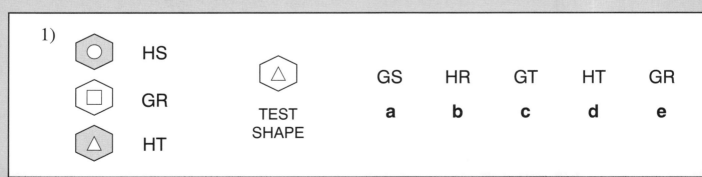

© 2016 Stephen Curran

2)

BX

AY

CX

TEST SHAPE

	BY	AX	CY	BX	AY
	a	**b**	**c**	**d**	**e**

3)

QG

RH

SH

TEST SHAPE

	SH	RH	SG	QH	RG
	a	**b**	**c**	**d**	**e**

4)

WK

XL

WM

TEST SHAPE

	XK	WM	XM	WK	WL
	a	**b**	**c**	**d**	**e**

5)

TF

UG

TE

TEST SHAPE

	UE	TG	TF	UF	UG
	a	**b**	**c**	**d**	**e**

6)

MR

NT

NS

TEST SHAPE

	MT	MS	NT	MR	NS
	a	**b**	**c**	**d**	**e**

GO ON TO THE NEXT PAGE

7)

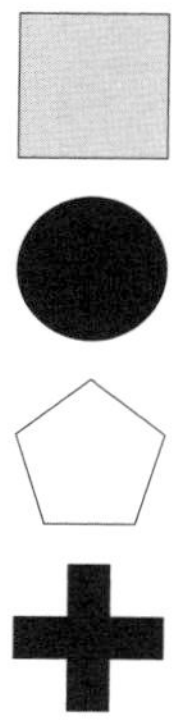

ME			NE	LE	MC	ND	LC

ME

ND

LF

NC

TEST SHAPE

NE	LE	MC	ND	LC
a	**b**	**c**	**d**	**e**

8)

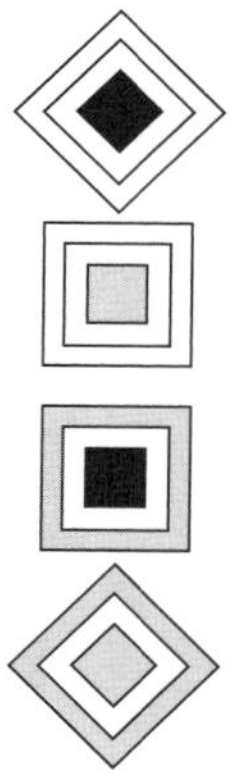

CH

CG

DH

DG

TEST SHAPE

CH	DG	CG	DF	DH
a	**b**	**c**	**d**	**e**

9)

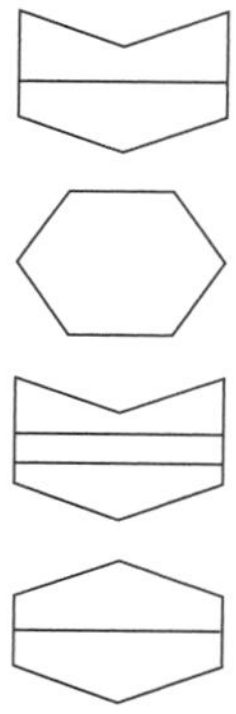

JB

LA

JC

KB

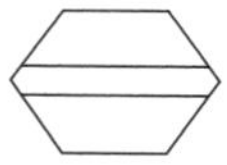

TEST SHAPE

LB	JA	KC	KA	LC
a	**b**	**c**	**d**	**e**

10)

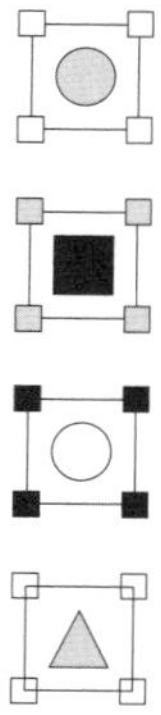

BP

CR

DP

BQ

TEST SHAPE

AP	DQ	AR	CQ	BR
a	**b**	**c**	**d**	**e**

GO ON TO THE NEXT PAGE

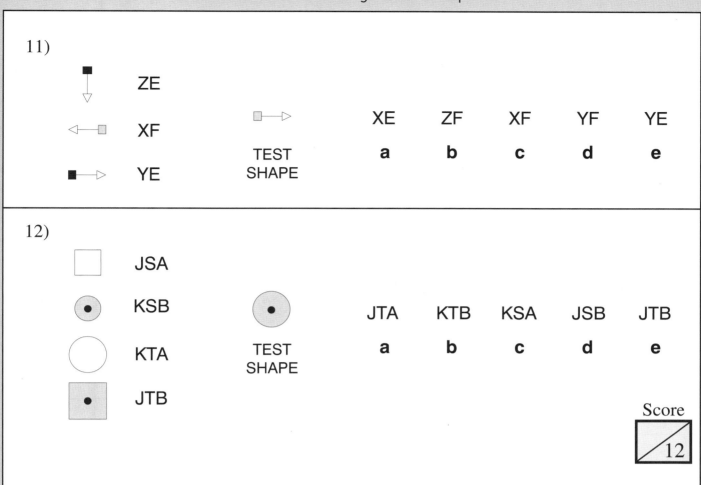

11)

ZE

XF

YE

TEST SHAPE

XE	ZF	XF	YF	YE
a	**b**	**c**	**d**	**e**

12)

JSA

KSB

KTA

JTB

TEST SHAPE

JTA	KTB	KSA	JSB	JTB
a	**b**	**c**	**d**	**e**

Score

/12

GO ON TO THE NEXT PAGE

Section 3

To the left of each of the lines below there are five squares arranged in order. One of these squares has been left empty. Find which one of the five squares on the right should take the place of the empty square.

Example

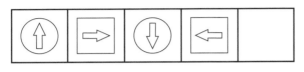 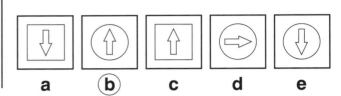

Now do the questions below. Circle the correct answer.

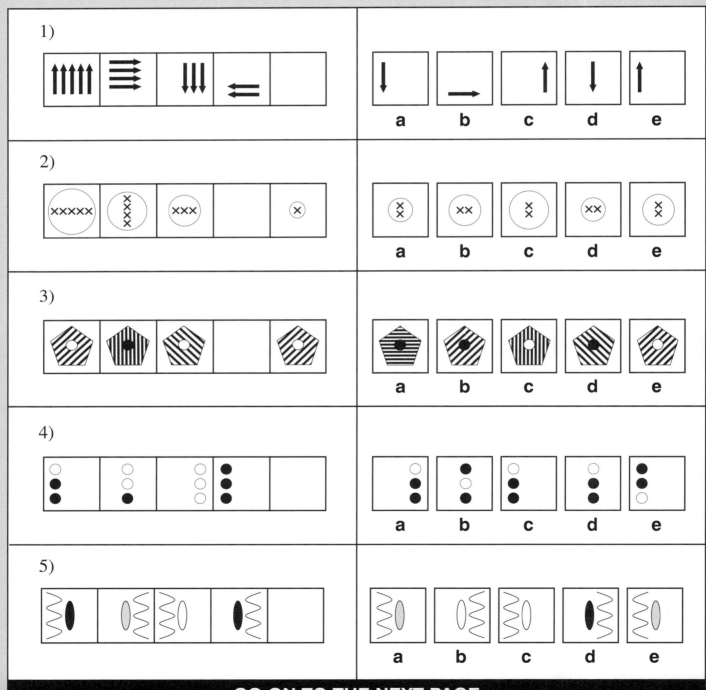

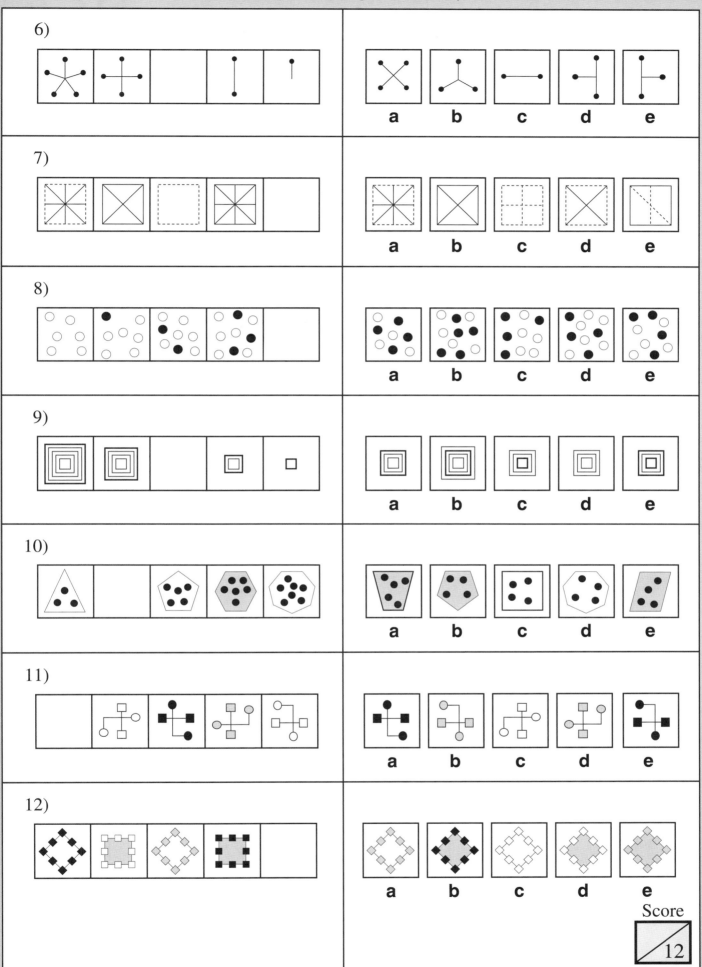

Section 4

In the big square on the left of each line below one of the small squares has been left empty. One of the five figures on the right should fill the empty square. Find this figure.

Example

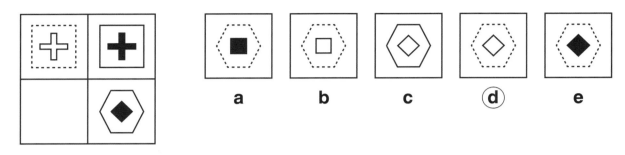

Now do the questions below. Circle the correct answer.

1)

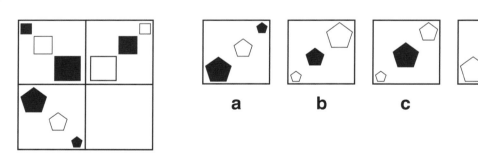

2)

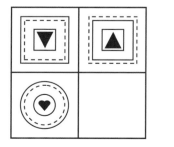

a   b   c   d   e

GO ON TO THE NEXT PAGE

3)

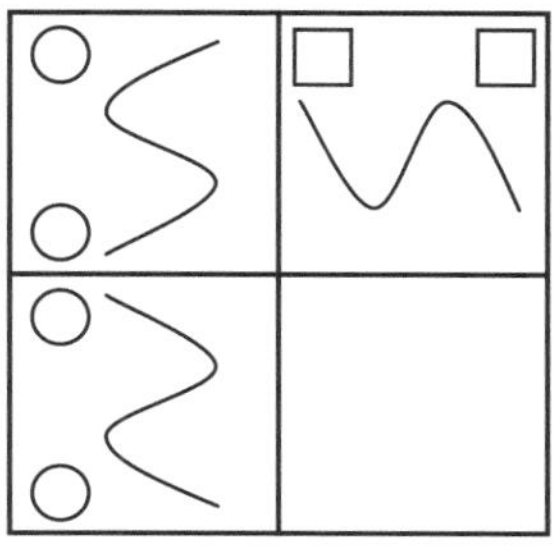

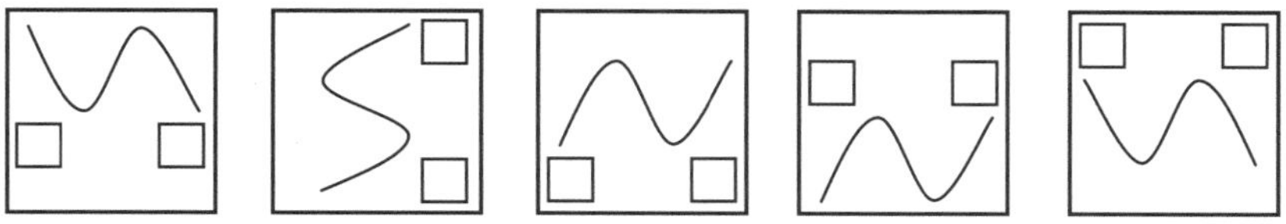

   a   b   c   d   e

4)

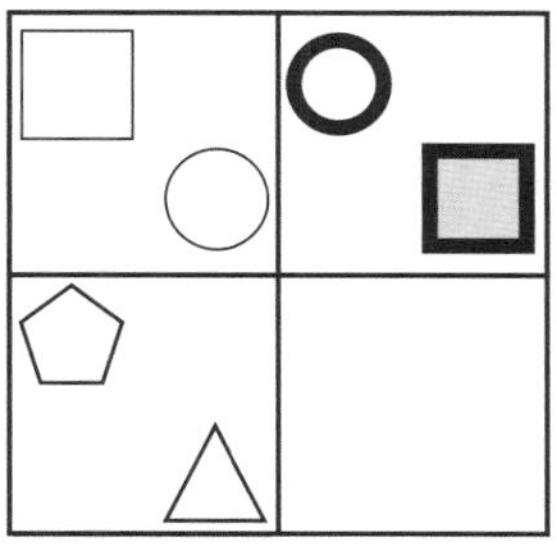

   a   b   c   d   e

5)

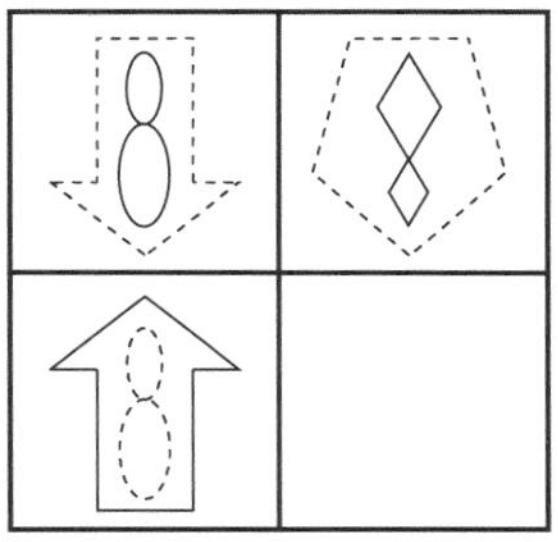

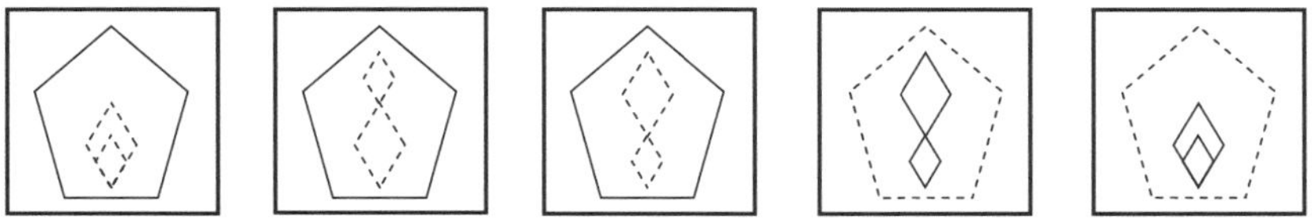

   a   b   c   d   e

6)

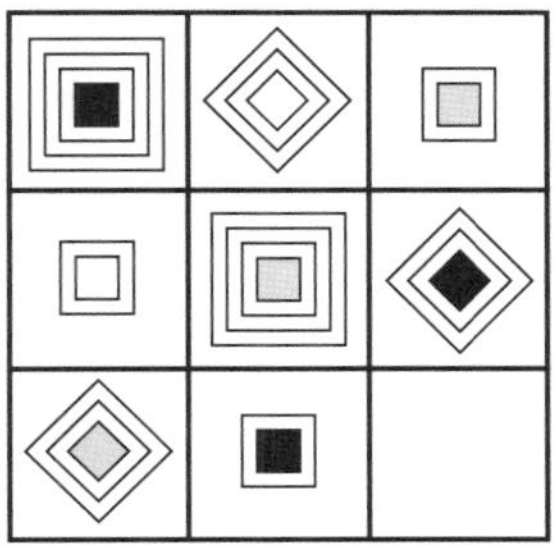

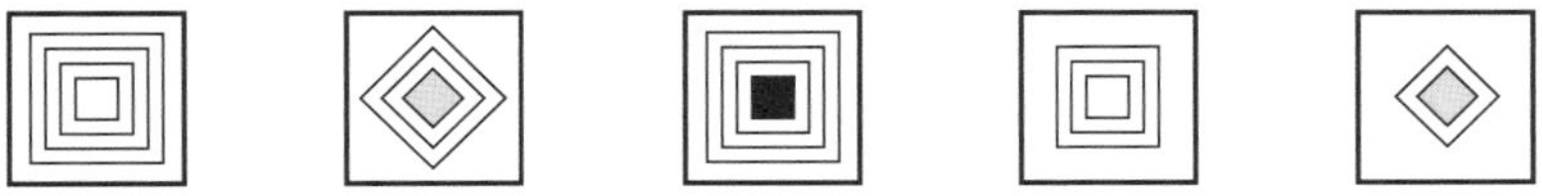

   a   b   c   d   e

7)

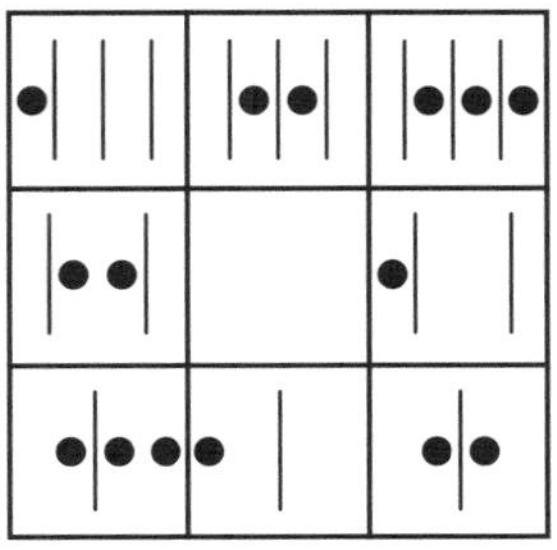

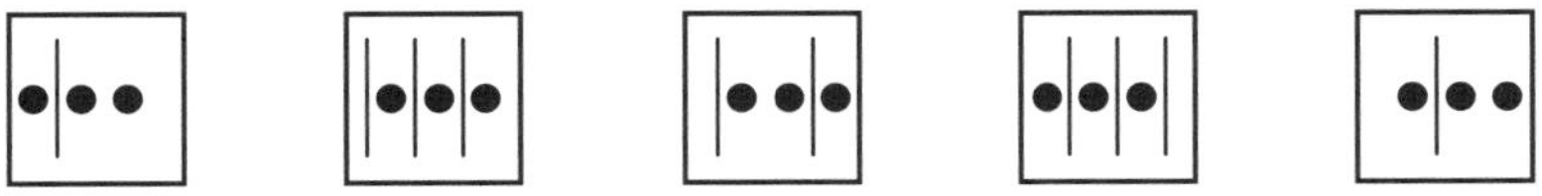

   a   b   c   d   e

GO ON TO THE NEXT PAGE

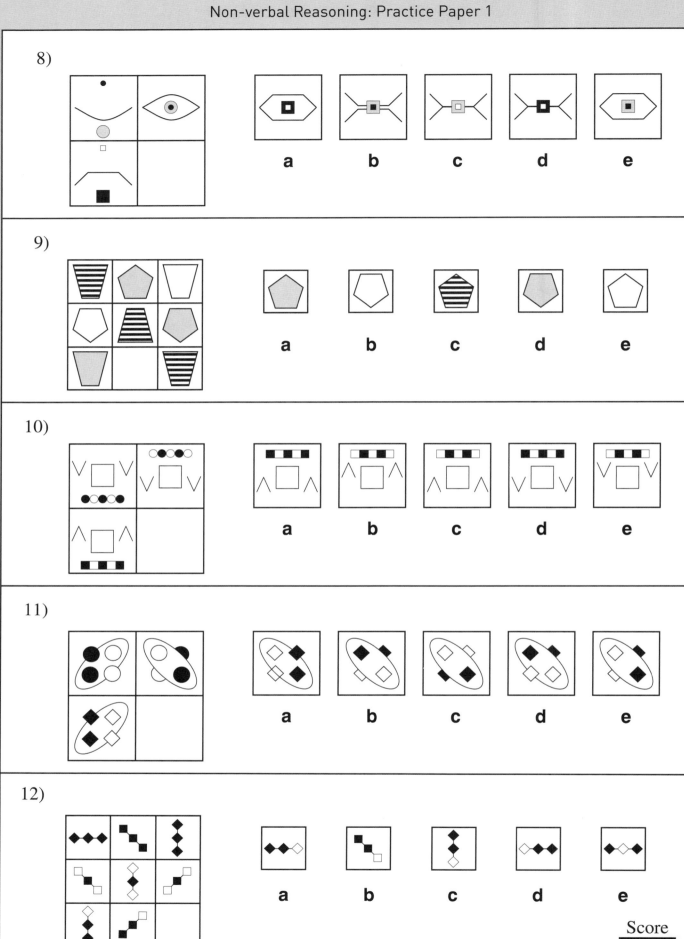

END OF PAPER

11+ Non-verbal Reasoning

Year 4/5

Testpack A

(GL Assessment Style)

Practice Paper 2

Please read the following before you start the Practice Paper:

1. Do not begin the Practice Paper until you are told to do so.

2. The Practice Paper contains 48 questions and you have 40 minutes to complete it.

3. Read the questions carefully so that you know what to do.

4. Try and answer as many questions as you can. Do not spend too much time on one question. If you cannot answer a question go on to the next one. If a question is omitted, ensure you have marked it clearly on your question paper, so it is easy to find it when you want to return to it after completing the rest of the paper.

5. If you are doing the Practice Paper as a standard test, circle your answer. If you want to change an answer, put a single line through the wrong answer and write the correct answer clearly.

    If you are doing the Practice Paper as a multiple-choice test, draw a clear line through your chosen box. If you want to change an answer, rub it out and mark the correct box clearly. **Do not write on or mark the answer sheet in any way other than that which has been specified.**

6. If you finish before your time ends, go back and check your answers.

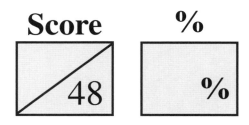

Section 1

To the left of each of the lines below there are five squares arranged in order. One of these squares has been left empty. Find which one of the five squares on the right should take the place of the empty square.

Example

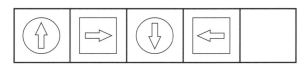 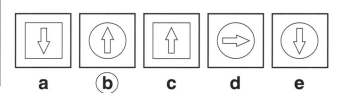

                                              a   b   c   d   e

Now do the questions below. Circle the correct answer.

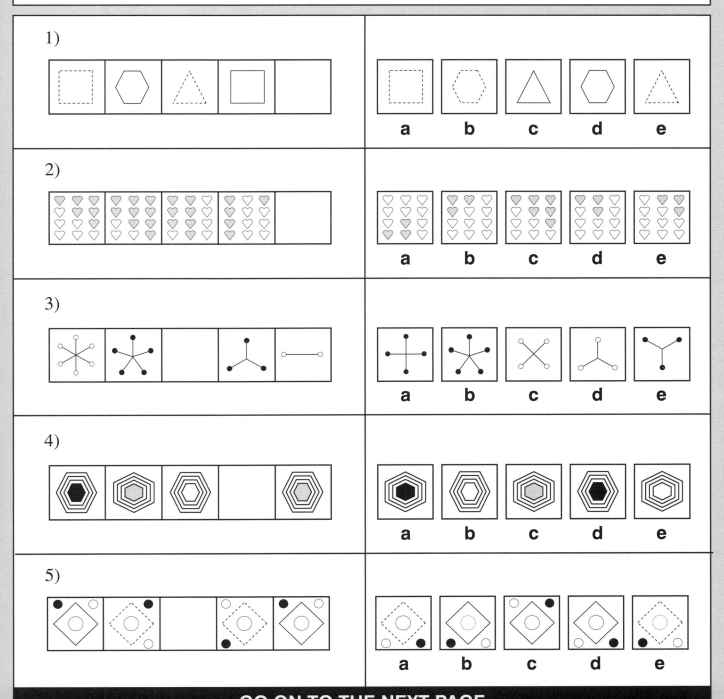

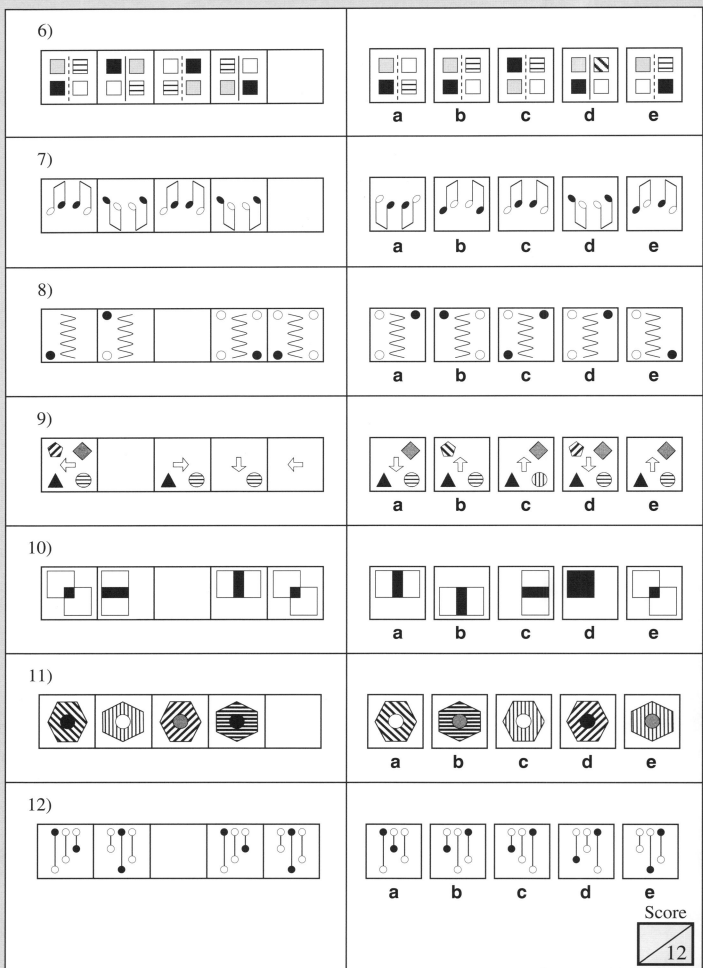

Score

/12

Section 2

On the left of each row are two shapes with an arrow between them. Decide how the second shape is related to the first. After these there is a third shape, then an arrow and then five more shapes. Decide which of the five shapes goes with the **third** shape to **make a pair** like the two shapes on the left.

Example

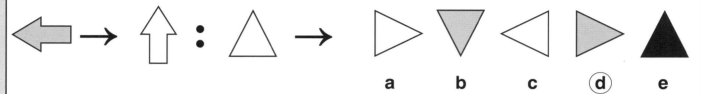

Now do the questions below. Circle the correct answer.

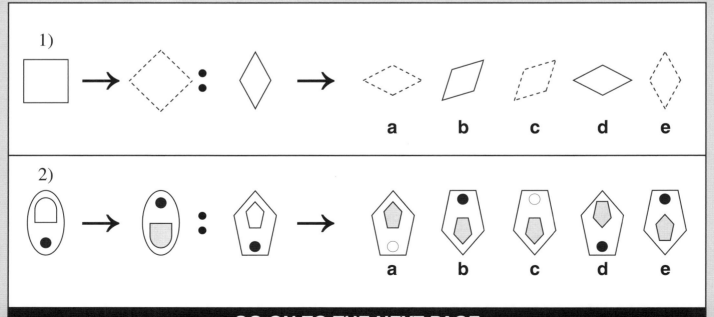

GO ON TO THE NEXT PAGE

© 2016 Stephen Curran

5

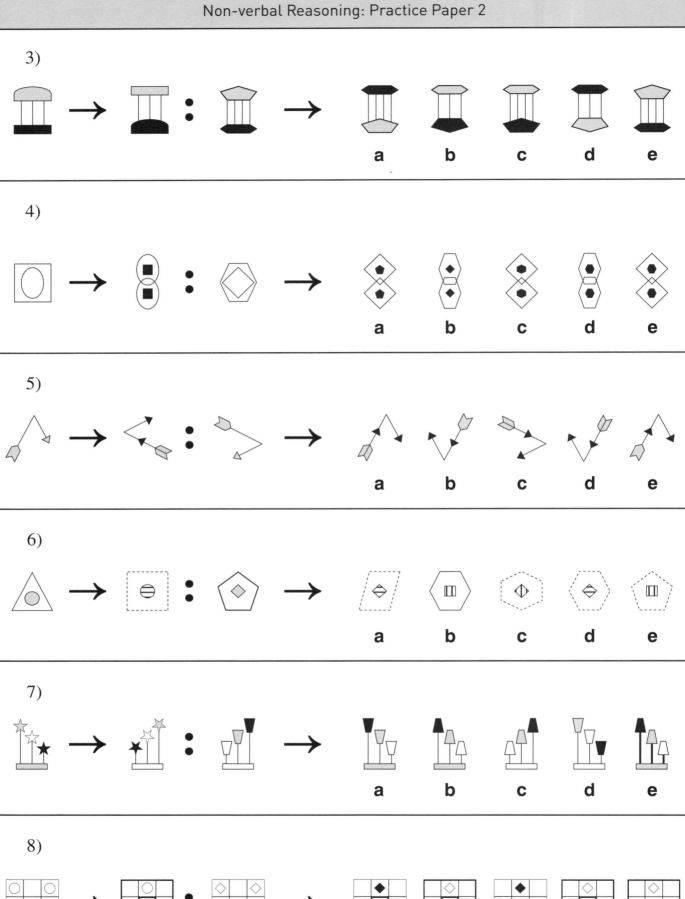

GO ON TO THE NEXT PAGE

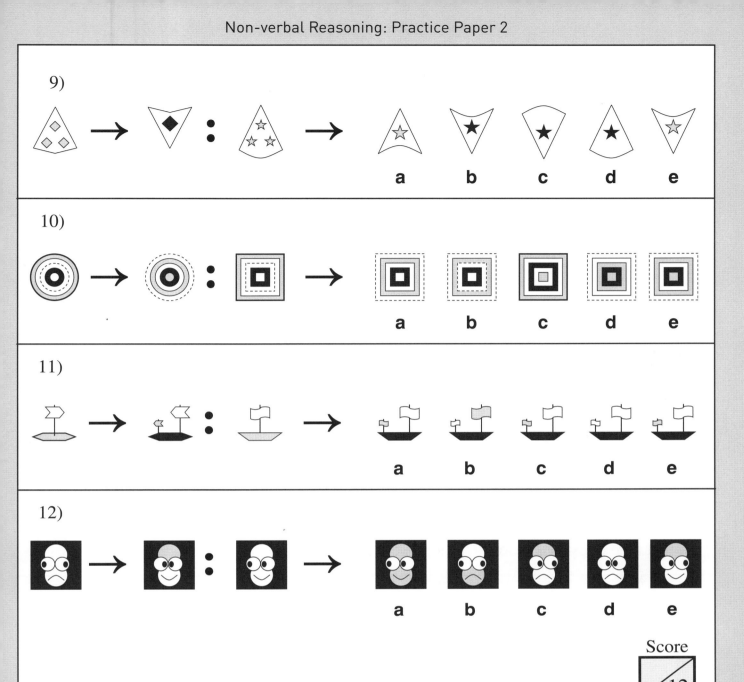

9)

10)

11)

12)

Score
12

GO ON TO THE NEXT PAGE

Section 3

The following shapes correspond to the codes below them. You must decide how the code letters go with the shapes and then find the correct code for the Test Shape.

Example

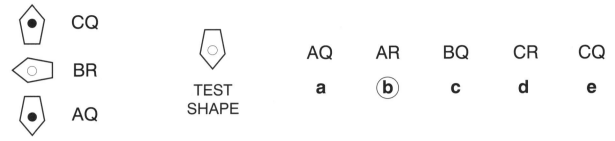

In this example each shape has two code letters. The first letter of each code refers to one aspect of the shape. Each shape has a different letter **A**, **B**, and **C**. What is different about each of the shapes? They are each turned in a different direction. The Test Shape points in the same direction as **A**, so its code letter must be **A**.

The second code letter refers to another aspect of the shape. Two of the shapes have the code **Q**. What is the same in the shapes? They both have black circles, whereas the shape with the code **R** has a white circle. The Test Shape has a white circle, and therefore the second code letter must be **R**.

Now we can tell that the code for the Test Shape must be **AR**.

Now do the questions below. Circle the correct answer.

1)

☐	TQ
⬡	SP
◯	TO

TEST SHAPE ◯

SQ	TP	SP	SO	TQ
a	**b**	**c**	**d**	**e**

GO ON TO THE NEXT PAGE

2)

					XC	YB	YA	XA	YC
	XB				a	b	c	d	e
	YC		TEST SHAPE						
	XA								

3)

					RN	SM	RL	SN	RM
	SL				a	b	c	d	e
	RN		TEST SHAPE						
	SM								

4)

					PC	QC	QE	PE	QD
	QC				a	b	c	d	e
	QE		TEST SHAPE						
	PD								

5)

					KZ	JZ	KX	JY	JX
	JZ				a	b	c	d	e
	JY		TEST SHAPE						
	KX								

6)

					NSE	MSF	NTE	MSE	NSF
	MSE				a	b	c	d	e
	MTF		TEST SHAPE						
	NSG								

GO ON TO THE NEXT PAGE

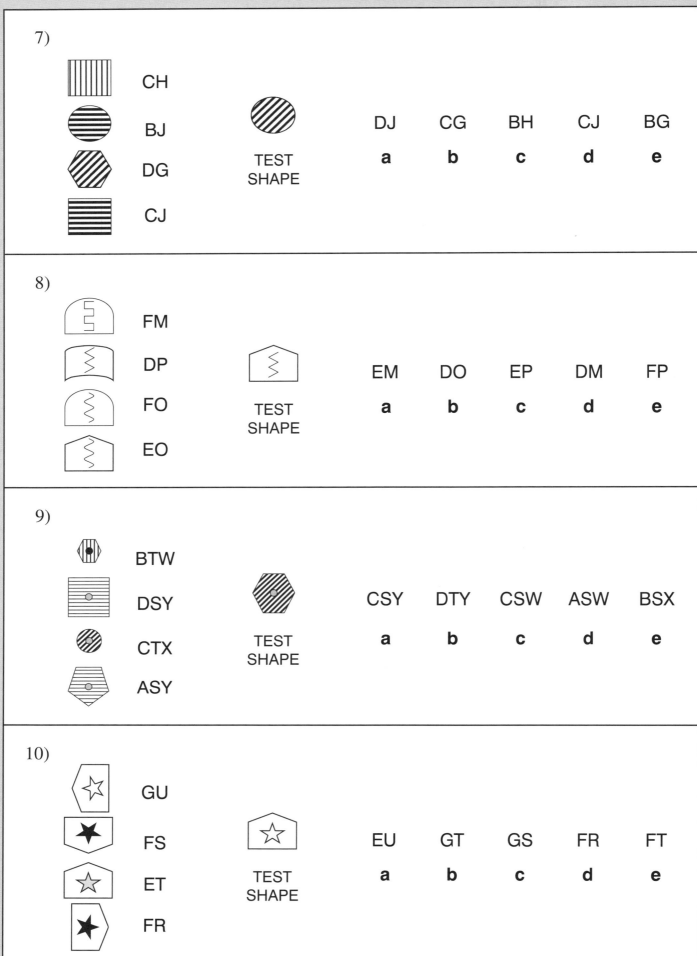

7)

		CH
		BJ
		DG
		CJ

TEST SHAPE

| DJ | CG | BH | CJ | BG |
| a | b | c | d | e |

8)

		FM
		DP
		FO
		EO

TEST SHAPE

| EM | DO | EP | DM | FP |
| a | b | c | d | e |

9)

		BTW
		DSY
		CTX
		ASY

TEST SHAPE

| CSY | DTY | CSW | ASW | BSX |
| a | b | c | d | e |

10)

		GU
		FS
		ET
		FR

TEST SHAPE

| EU | GT | GS | FR | FT |
| a | b | c | d | e |

GO ON TO THE NEXT PAGE

11)

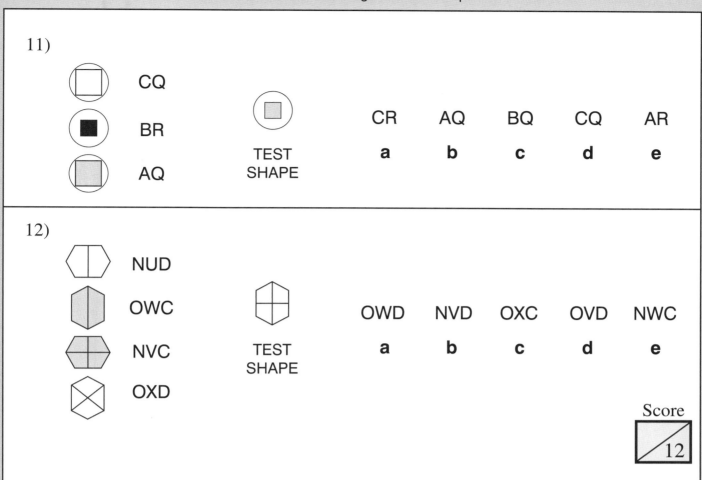

	CR	AQ	BQ	CQ	AR
	a	**b**	**c**	**d**	**e**

12)

	OWD	NVD	OXC	OVD	NWC
	a	**b**	**c**	**d**	**e**

Score

12

GO ON TO THE NEXT PAGE

Section 4

On the left of each of the rows below there are two figures that are alike. On the right there are five more figures. Find which one of these five is **most like** the two figures on the left.

Example

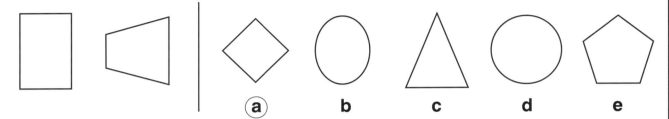

Now do the questions below. Circle the correct answer.

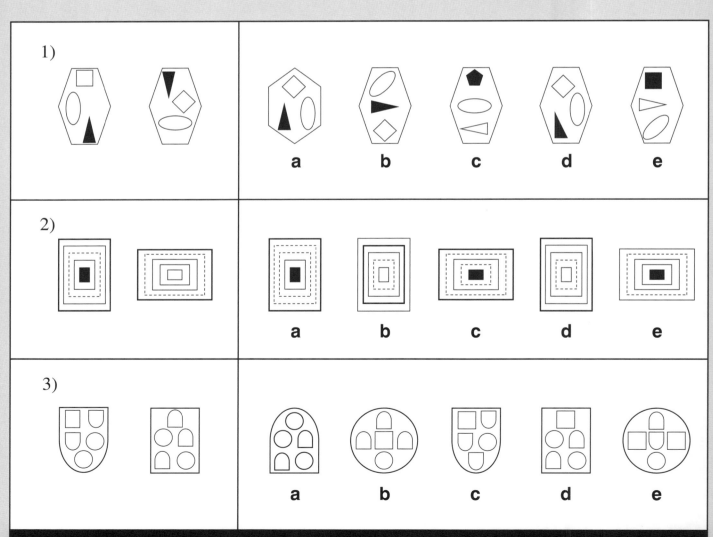

GO ON TO THE NEXT PAGE

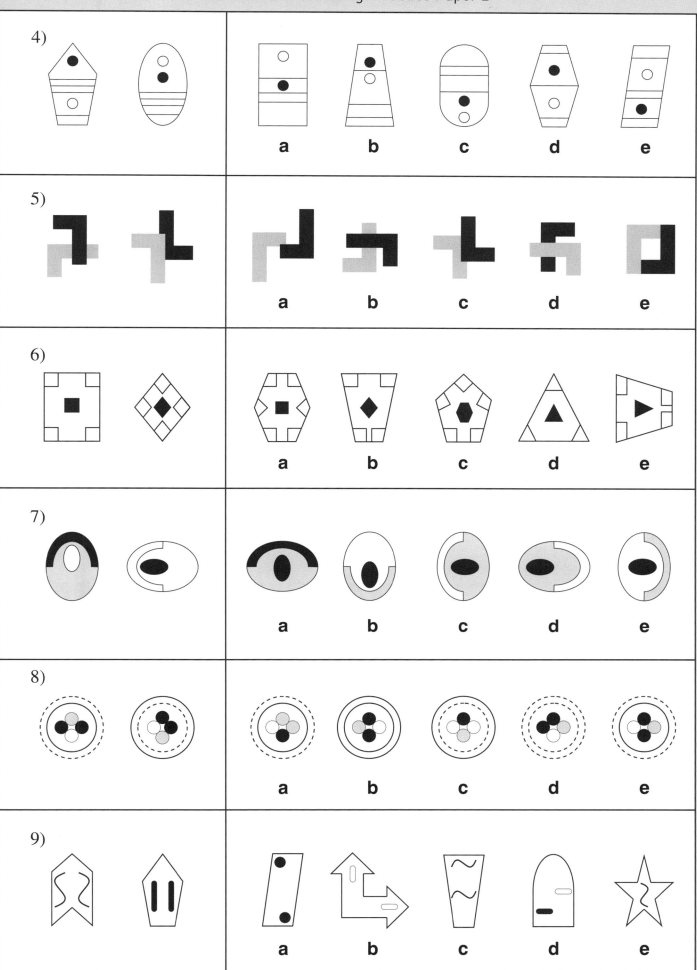

4)

a   b   c   d   e

5)

a   b   c   d   e

6)

a   b   c   d   e

7)

a   b   c   d   e

8)

a   b   c   d   e

9)

a   b   c   d   e

GO ON TO THE NEXT PAGE

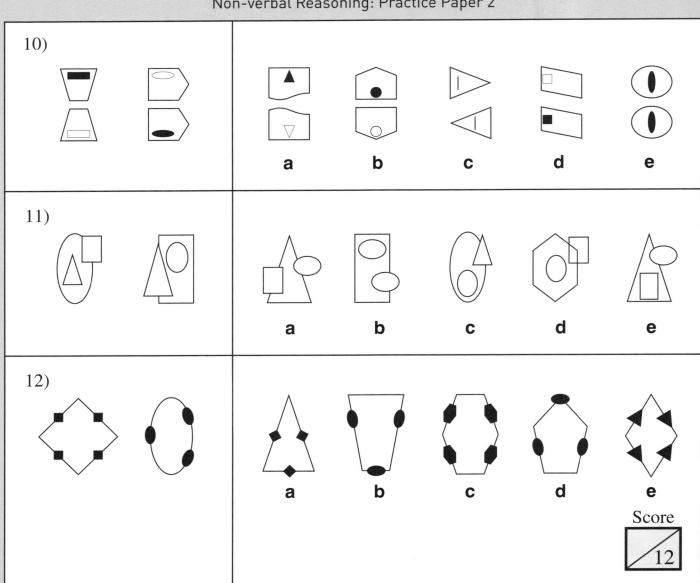

10)

a   b   c   d   e

11)

a   b   c   d   e

12)

a   b   c   d   e

Score

12

END OF PAPER

11+ Non-verbal Reasoning

Year 4/5

Testpack A

(GL Assessment Style)

Practice Paper 3

Please read the following before you start the Practice Paper:

1. Do not begin the Practice Paper until you are told to do so.

2. The Practice Paper contains 48 questions and you have 40 minutes to complete it.

3. Read the questions carefully so that you know what to do.

4. Try and answer as many questions as you can. Do not spend too much time on one question. If you cannot answer a question go on to the next one. If a question is omitted, ensure you have marked it clearly on your question paper, so it is easy to find it when you want to return to it after completing the rest of the paper.

5. If you are doing the Practice Paper as a standard test, circle your answer. If you want to change an answer, put a single line through the wrong answer and write the correct answer clearly.

    If you are doing the Practice Paper as a multiple-choice test, draw a clear line through your chosen box. If you want to change an answer, rub it out and mark the correct box clearly. **Do not write on or mark the answer sheet in any way other than that which has been specified.**

6. If you finish before your time ends, go back and check your answers.

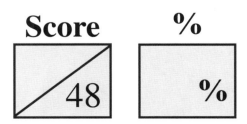

Section 1

The following shapes correspond to the codes next to them. You must decide how the code letters go with the shapes and then find the correct code for the Test Shape.

Example

TEST
SHAPE

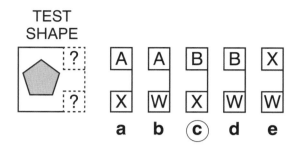

On the top row the code letter **A** appears twice. What is similar about these two shapes? They are both triangles. The code letter **W** appears twice below the shapes. What is similar about these shapes? They both have a White Fill. Looking at the Test Shape we can see that it is a pentagon, which means that the first code letter should be **B**. It also has a Grey Fill, which means that the second code letter should be **X**. Therefore the answer is c. **BX**

Now do the questions below. Circle the correct answer.

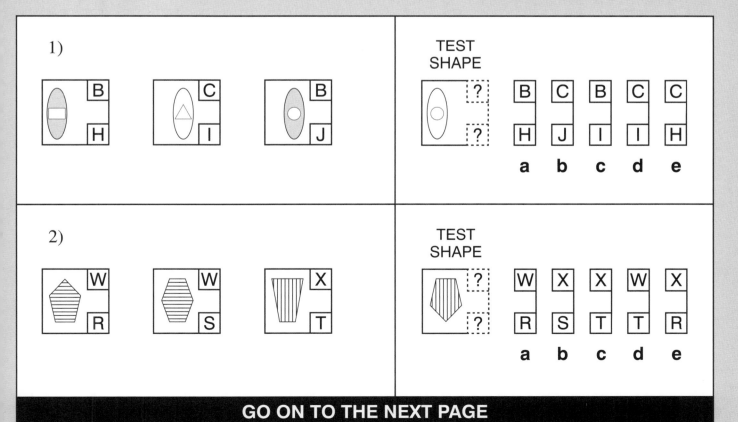

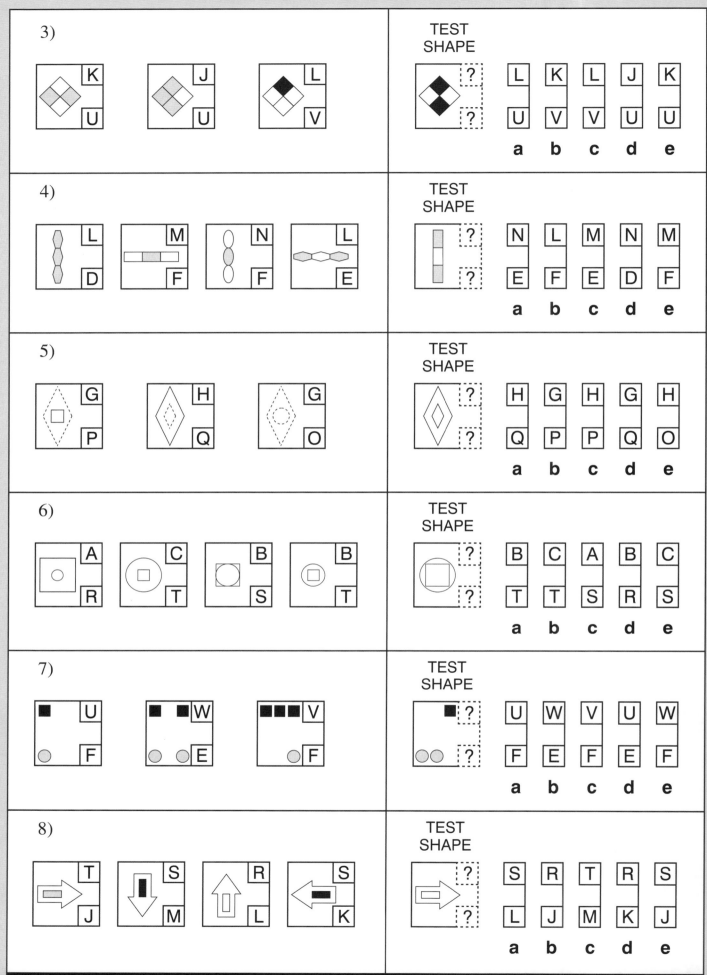

3)

TEST SHAPE

L U	K V	L V	J U	K U
a	**b**	**c**	**d**	**e**

4)

TEST SHAPE

N E	L F	M E	N D	M F
a	**b**	**c**	**d**	**e**

5)

TEST SHAPE

H Q	G P	H P	G Q	H O
a	**b**	**c**	**d**	**e**

6)

TEST SHAPE

B T	C T	A S	B R	C S
a	**b**	**c**	**d**	**e**

7)

TEST SHAPE

U F	W E	V F	U E	W F
a	**b**	**c**	**d**	**e**

8)

TEST SHAPE

S L	R J	T M	R K	S J
a	**b**	**c**	**d**	**e**

GO ON TO THE NEXT PAGE

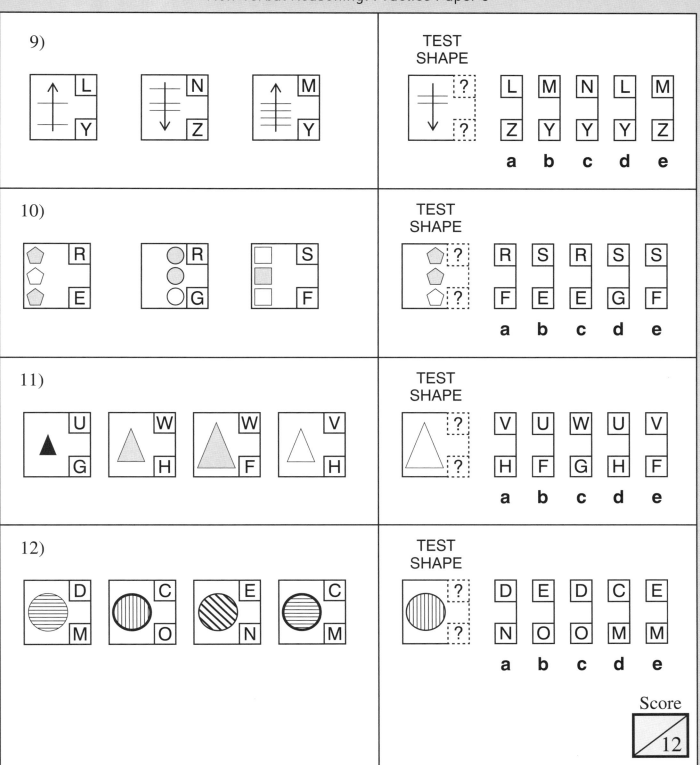

9)

TEST SHAPE

L	M	N	L	M
Z	Y	Y	Y	Z
a	b	c	d	e

10)

TEST SHAPE

R	S	R	S	S
F	E	E	G	F
a	b	c	d	e

11)

TEST SHAPE

V	U	W	U	V
H	F	G	H	F
a	b	c	d	e

12)

TEST SHAPE

D	E	D	C	E
N	O	O	M	M
a	b	c	d	e

Score /12

GO ON TO THE NEXT PAGE

Section 2

On the left of each of the rows below there are two figures that are alike. On the right there are five more figures. Find which one of these five is **most like** the two figures on the left.

Example

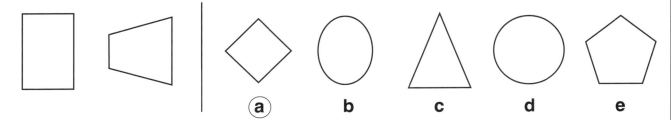

Now do the questions below. Circle the correct answer.

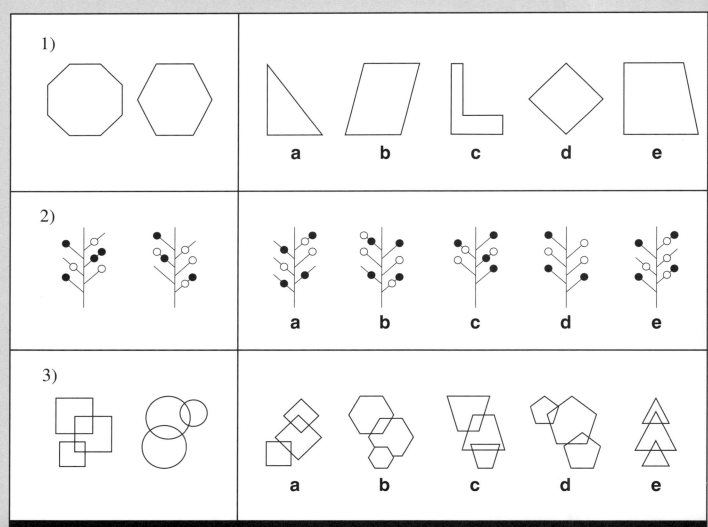

GO ON TO THE NEXT PAGE

© 2016 Stephen Curran

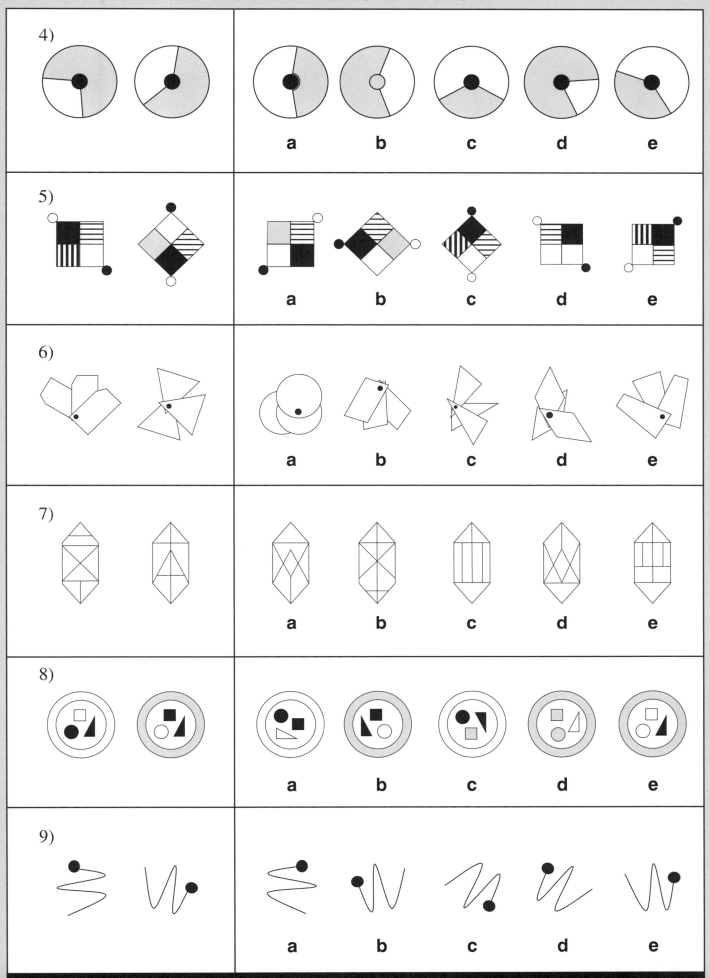

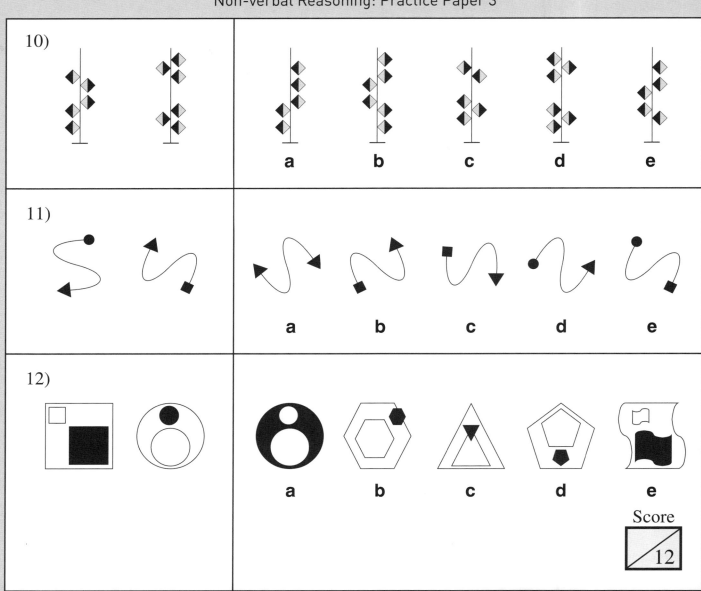

Section 3

In the big square on the left of each line below one of the small squares has been left empty. One of the five figures on the right should fill the empty square. Find this figure.

Example

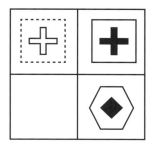   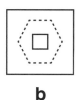   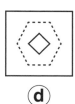   

                                           a   **b**   **c**   **(d)**   **e**

Now do the questions below. Circle the correct answer.

1)

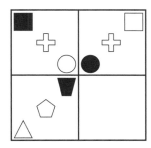   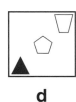

                                           a   **b**   **c**   **d**   **e**

2)

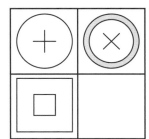

                                           a   **b**   **c**   **d**   **e**

GO ON TO THE NEXT PAGE

3)

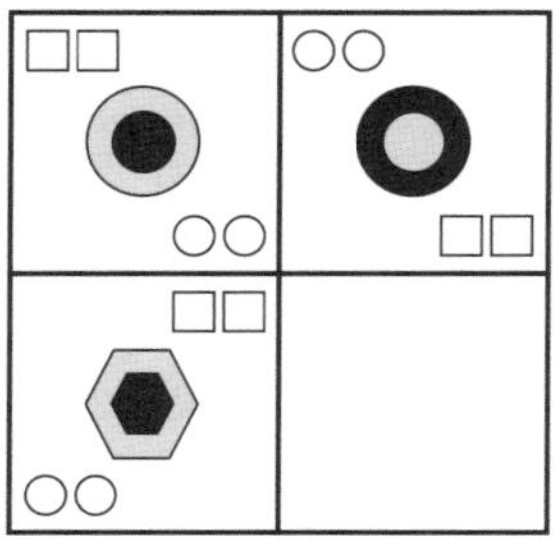

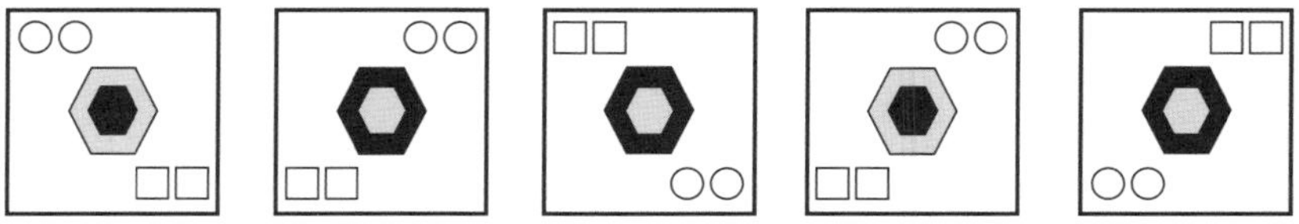

a b c d e

4)

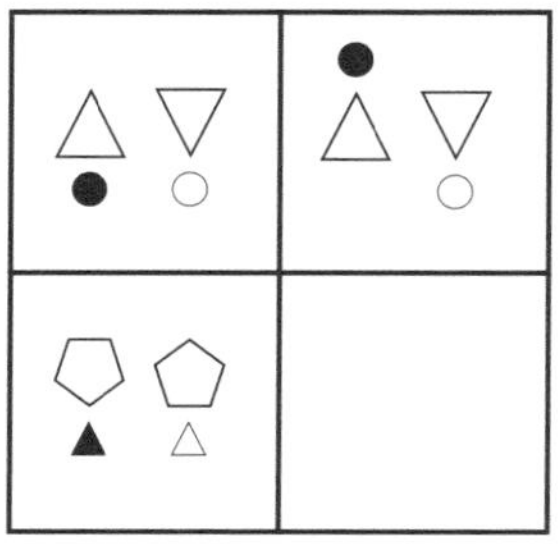

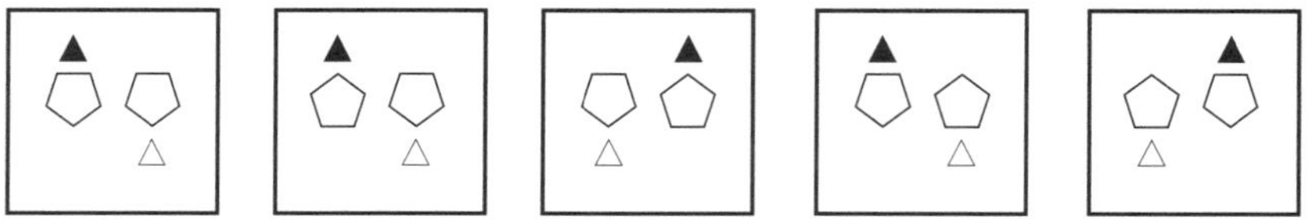

a b c d e

5)

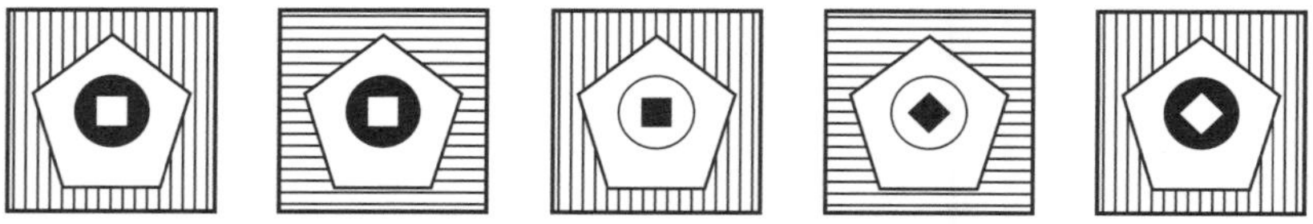

a b c d e

6)

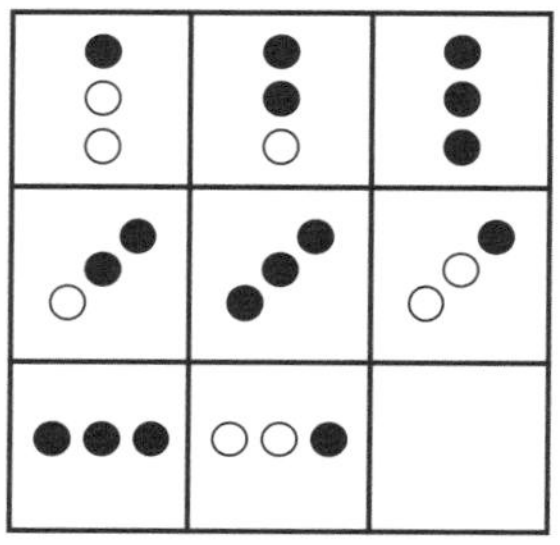

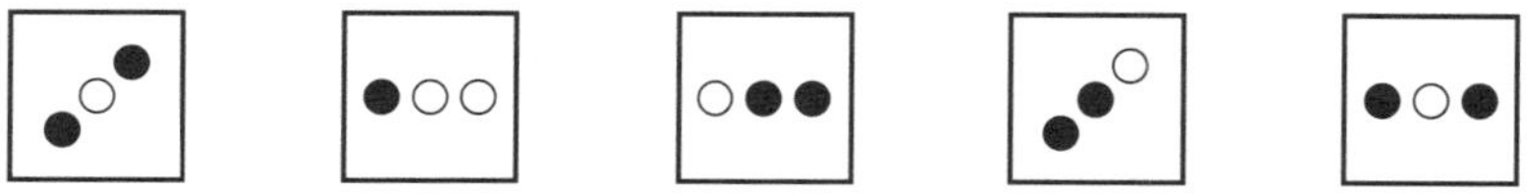

a b c d e

7)

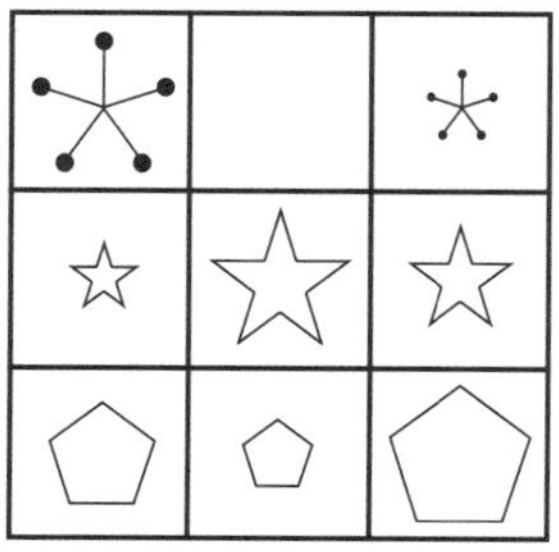

a b c d e

GO ON TO THE NEXT PAGE

8)

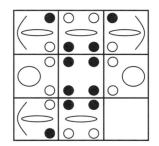

    a   **b**   **c**   **d**   **e**

9)

    a   **b**   **c**   **d**   **e**

10)

    a   **b**   **c**   **d**   **e**

11)

    a   **b**   **c**   **d**   **e**

12)

    a   **b**   **c**   **d**   **e**

Score

GO ON TO THE NEXT PAGE

Section 4

On the left of each row are two shapes with an arrow between them. Decide how the second shape is related to the first. After these there is a third shape, then an arrow and then five more shapes. Decide which of the five shapes goes with the **third** shape to **make a pair** like the two shapes on the left.

Example

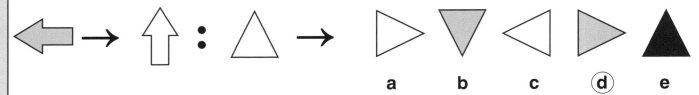

Now do the questions below. Circle the correct answer.

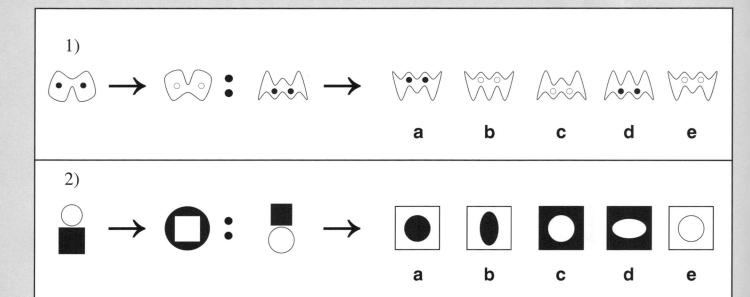

GO ON TO THE NEXT PAGE

　　　　　　　　　　　　　　　　　　© 2016 Stephen Curran

3)

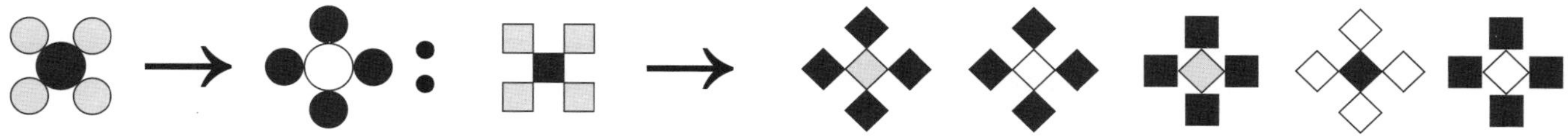

a   b   c   d   e

4)

a   b   c   d   e

5)

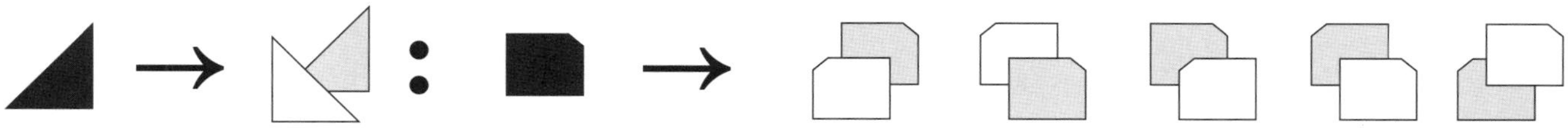

a   b   c   d   e

6)

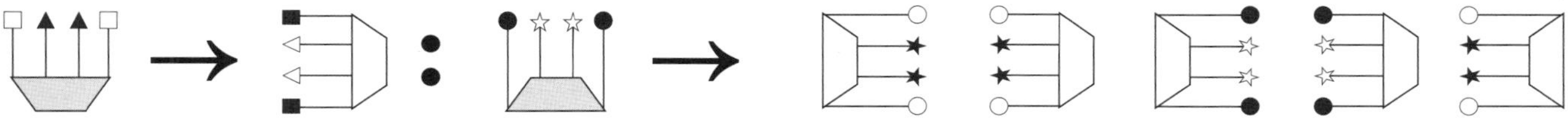

a   b   c   d   e

7)

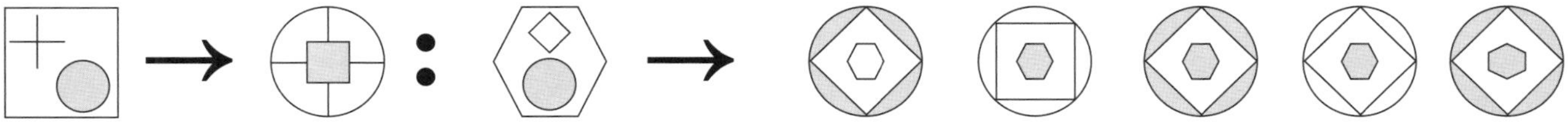

a   b   c   d   e

8)

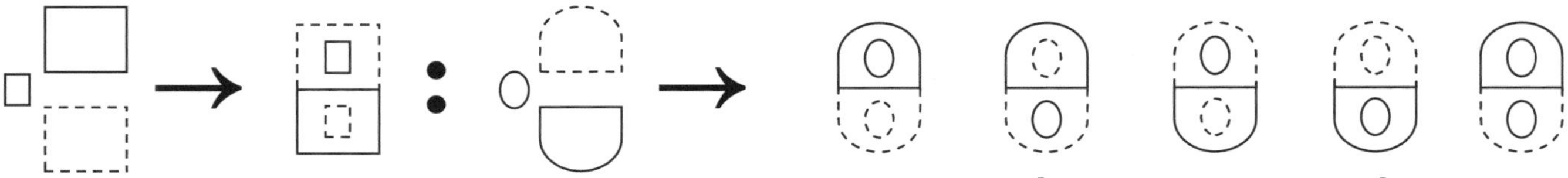

a   b   c   d   e

GO ON TO THE NEXT PAGE

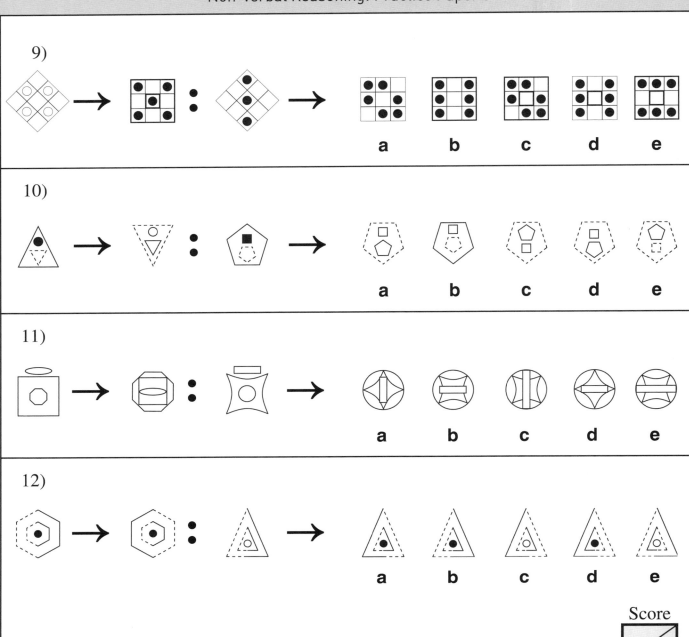

9)

10)

11)

12)

Score
/12

END OF PAPER

11+ Non-verbal Reasoning

Year 4/5

Testpack A

(GL Assessment Style)

Practice Paper 4

Please read the following before you start the Practice Paper:

1. Do not begin the Practice Paper until you are told to do so.

2. The Practice Paper contains 48 questions and you have 40 minutes to complete it.

3. Read the questions carefully so that you know what to do.

4. Try and answer as many questions as you can. Do not spend too much time on one question. If you cannot answer a question go on to the next one. If a question is omitted, ensure you have marked it clearly on your question paper, so it is easy to find it when you want to return to it after completing the rest of the paper.

5. If you are doing the Practice Paper as a standard test, circle your answer. If you want to change an answer, put a single line through the wrong answer and write the correct answer clearly.

    If you are doing the Practice Paper as a multiple-choice test, draw a clear line through your chosen box. If you want to change an answer, rub it out and mark the correct box clearly. **Do not write on or mark the answer sheet in any way other than that which has been specified.**

6. If you finish before your time ends, go back and check your answers.

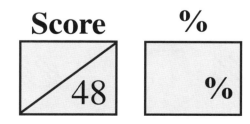

Section 1

On the left of each of the rows below there are two figures that are alike. On the right there are five more figures. Find which one of these five is **most like** the two figures on the left.

Example

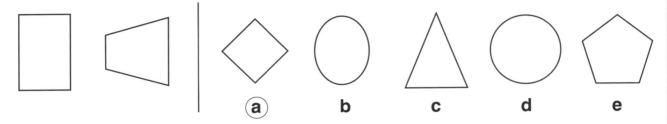

a   b   c   d   e

Now do the questions below. Circle the correct answer.

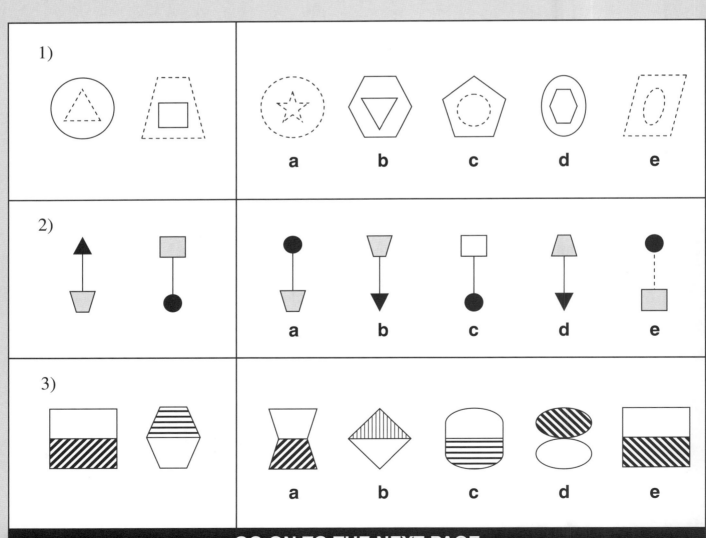

GO ON TO THE NEXT PAGE

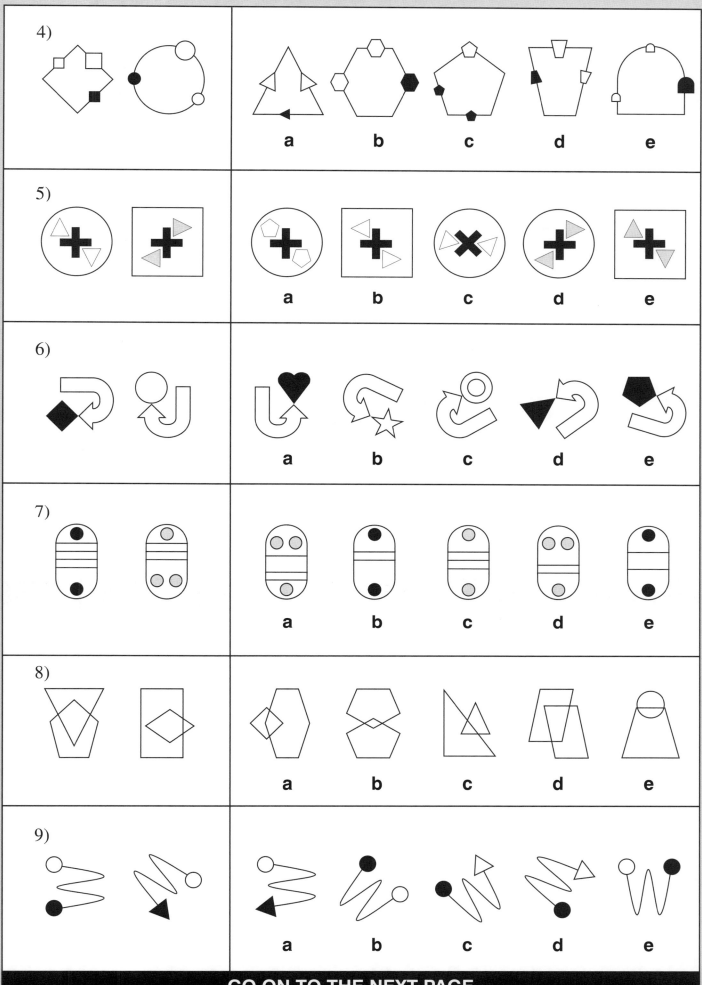

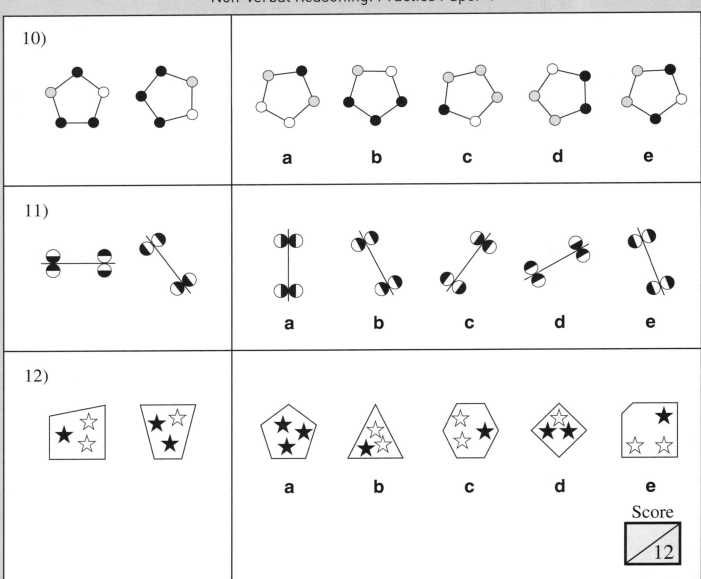

10)

11)

12)

Score

/12

GO ON TO THE NEXT PAGE

Section 2

The following shapes correspond to the codes next to them. You must decide how the code letters go with the shapes and then find the correct code for the Test Shape.

Example

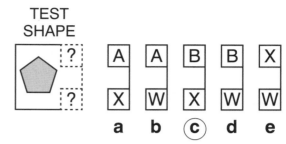

On the top row the code letter **A** appears twice. What is similar about these two shapes? They are both triangles. The code letter **W** appears twice below the shapes. What is similar about these shapes? They both have a White Fill. Looking at the Test Shape we can see that it is a pentagon, which means that the first code letter should be **B**. It also has a Grey Fill, which means that the second code letter should be **X**. Therefore the answer is c. **BX**

Now do the questions below. Circle the correct answer.

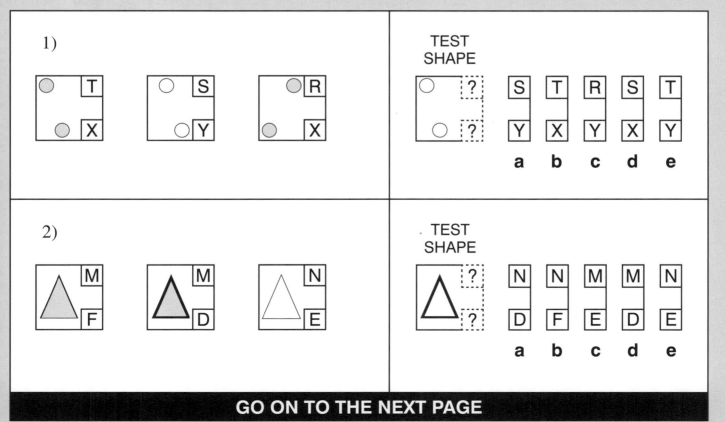

1)

2)

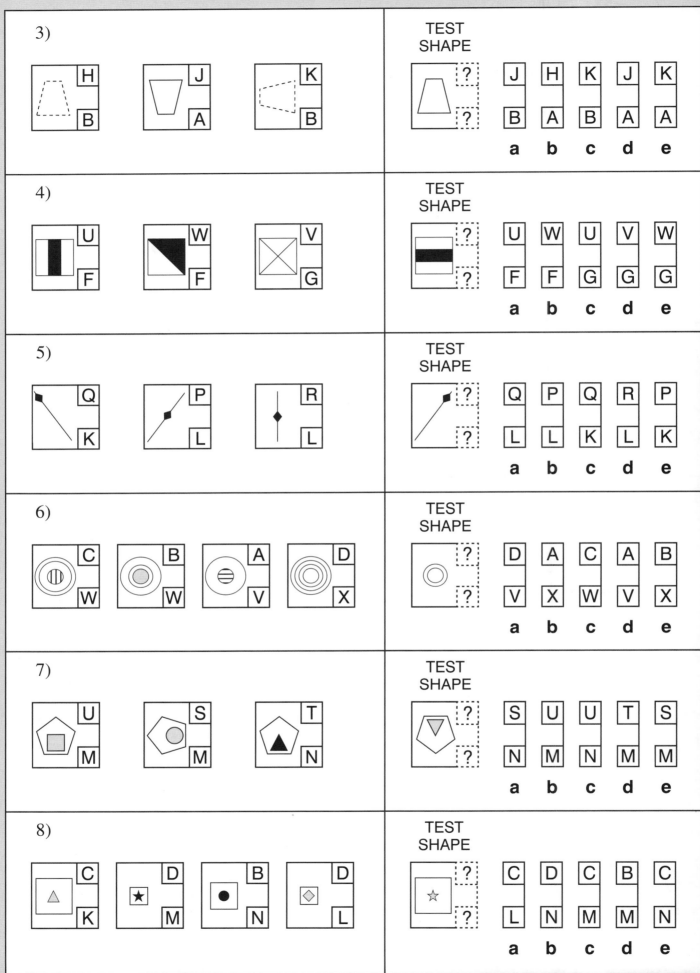

© 2016 Stephen Curran ae

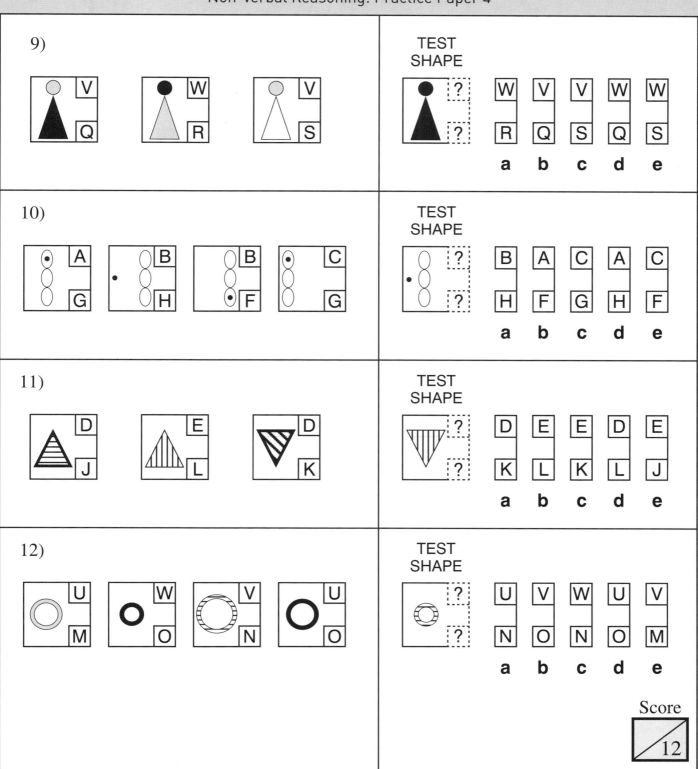

7

Section 3

In each of the rows below there are five figures. Find one figure in each row that is **most unlike** the other four.

Example

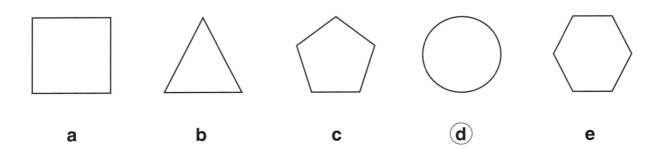

a   b   c   ⓓ   e

Now do the questions below. Circle the correct answer.

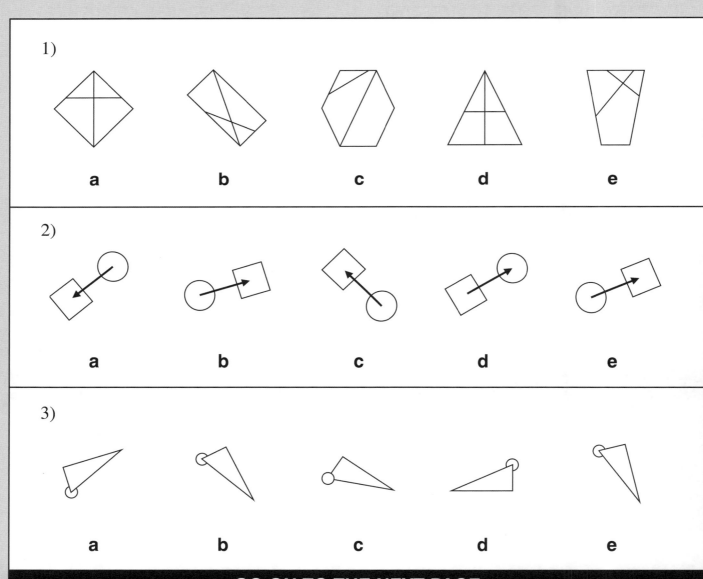

1)

a   b   c   d   e

2)

a   b   c   d   e

3)

a   b   c   d   e

GO ON TO THE NEXT PAGE

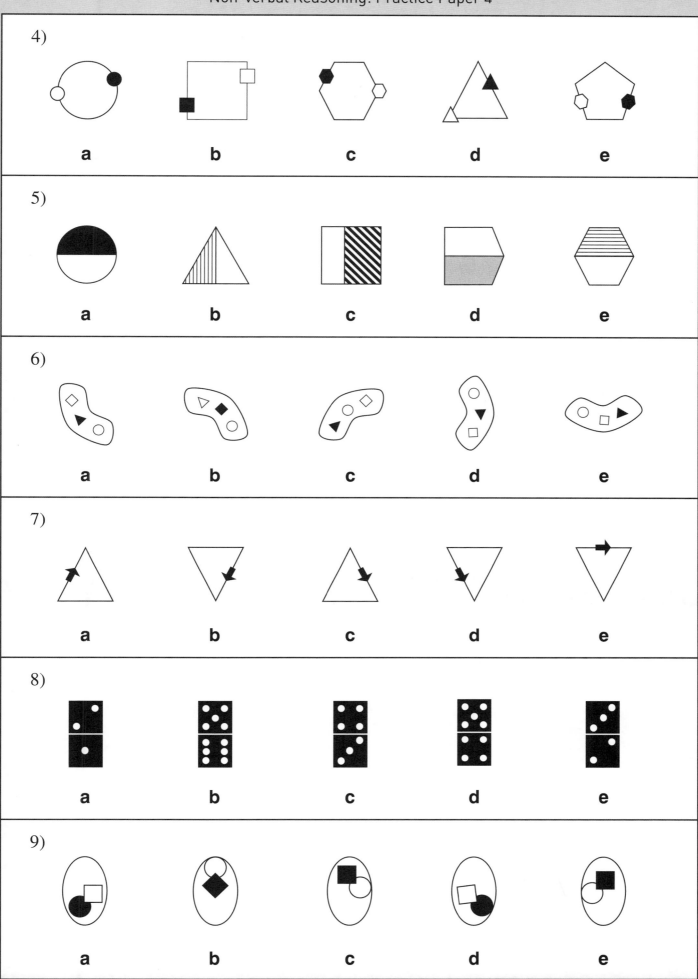

4)

    a   b   c   d   e

5)

    a   b   c   d   e

6)

    a   b   c   d   e

7)

    a   b   c   d   e

8)

    a   b   c   d   e

9)

    a   b   c   d   e

GO ON TO THE NEXT PAGE

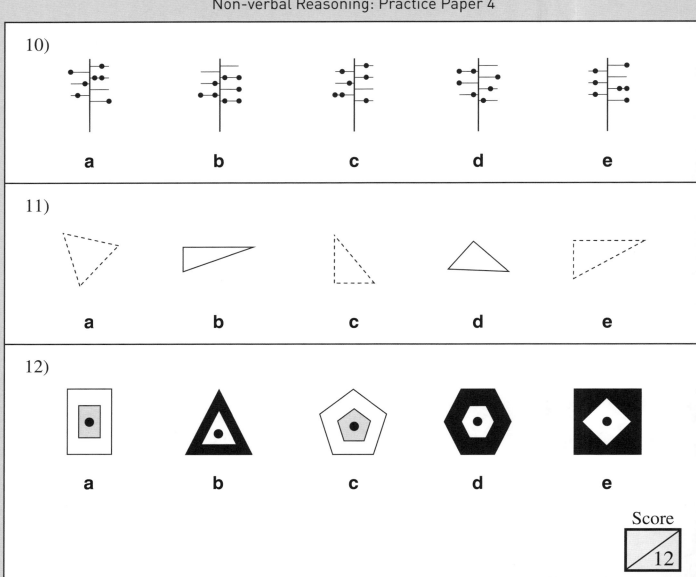

10)

    a   b   c   d   e

11)

    a   b   c   d   e

12)

    a   b   c   d   e

Score
/12

GO ON TO THE NEXT PAGE

Section 4

To the left of each of the lines below there are five squares arranged in order. One of these squares has been left empty. Find which one of the five squares on the right should take the place of the empty square.

Example

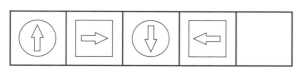 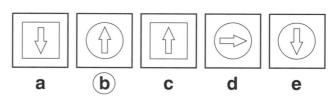

Now do the questions below. Circle the correct answer.

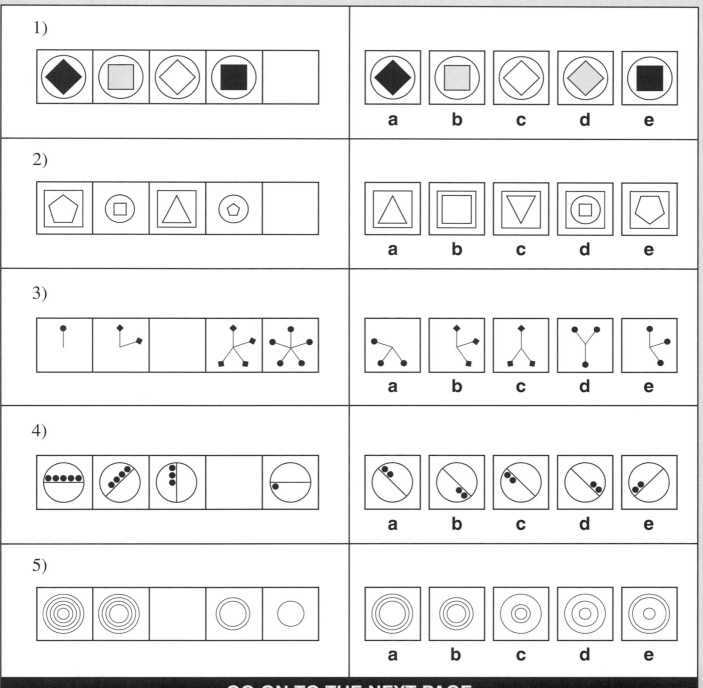

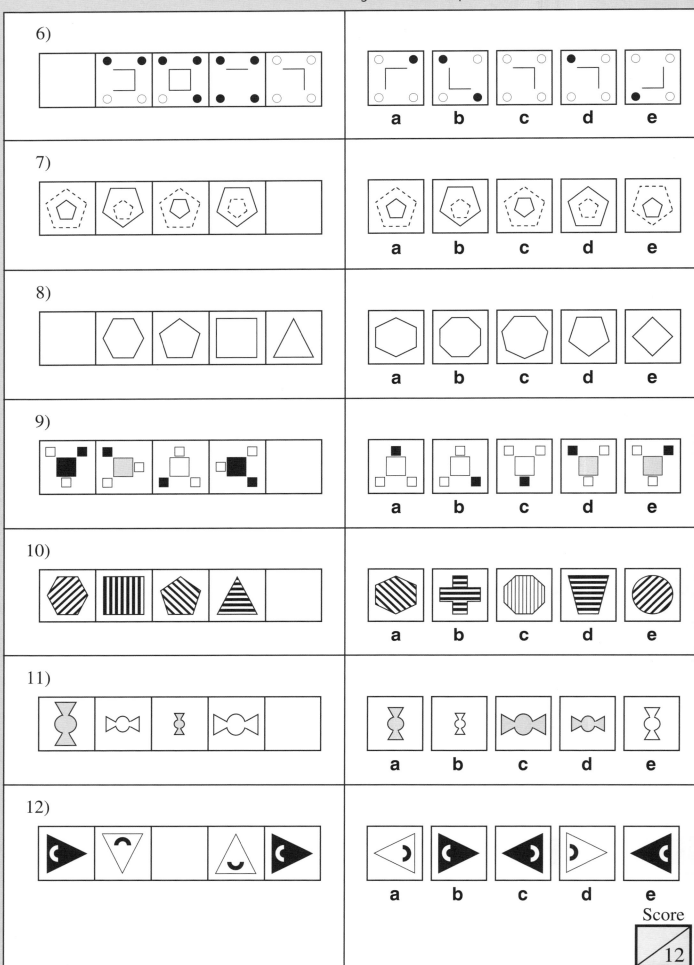

Score

12

END OF PAPER

© 2016 Stephen Curran ae

Multiple-choice Answer Sheets

11+ Non-verbal Reasoning Year 4/5 Testpack A Practice Paper 1

Section 1

	EXAMPLE	1	2	3	4	5
A	▭	▭	▭	▭	▭	▭
B	▭	▭	▭	▭	▭	▭
C	▭	▭	▭	▭	▭	▭
D	▬	▭	▭	▭	▭	▭
E	▭	▭	▭	▭	▭	▭

	6	7	8	9	10	11	12
A	▭	▭	▭	▭	▭	▭	▭
B	▭	▭	▭	▭	▭	▭	▭
C	▭	▭	▭	▭	▭	▭	▭
D	▭	▭	▭	▭	▭	▭	▭
E	▭	▭	▭	▭	▭	▭	▭

Section 2

	EXAMPLE	1	2	3	4	5
A	▭	▭	▭	▭	▭	▭
B	▬	▭	▭	▭	▭	▭
C	▭	▭	▭	▭	▭	▭
D	▭	▭	▭	▭	▭	▭
E	▭	▭	▭	▭	▭	▭

	6	7	8	9	10	11	12
A	▭	▭	▭	▭	▭	▭	▭
B	▭	▭	▭	▭	▭	▭	▭
C	▭	▭	▭	▭	▭	▭	▭
D	▭	▭	▭	▭	▭	▭	▭
E	▭	▭	▭	▭	▭	▭	▭

Section 3

	EXAMPLE	1	2	3	4	5
A	▭	▭	▭	▭	▭	▭
B	▬	▭	▭	▭	▭	▭
C	▭	▭	▭	▭	▭	▭
D	▭	▭	▭	▭	▭	▭
E	▭	▭	▭	▭	▭	▭

	6	7	8	9	10	11	12
A	▭	▭	▭	▭	▭	▭	▭
B	▭	▭	▭	▭	▭	▭	▭
C	▭	▭	▭	▭	▭	▭	▭
D	▭	▭	▭	▭	▭	▭	▭
E	▭	▭	▭	▭	▭	▭	▭

Section 4

	EXAMPLE	1	2	3	4	5
A	▭	▭	▭	▭	▭	▭
B	▭	▭	▭	▭	▭	▭
C	▭	▭	▭	▭	▭	▭
D	▬	▭	▭	▭	▭	▭
E	▭	▭	▭	▭	▭	▭

	6	7	8	9	10	11	12
A	▭	▭	▭	▭	▭	▭	▭
B	▭	▭	▭	▭	▭	▭	▭
C	▭	▭	▭	▭	▭	▭	▭
D	▭	▭	▭	▭	▭	▭	▭
E	▭	▭	▭	▭	▭	▭	▭

Section 1

EXAMPLE
- A ▢
- B ▬
- C ▢
- D ▢
- E ▢

1
- A ▢
- B ▢
- C ▢
- D ▢
- E ▢

2
- A ▢
- B ▢
- C ▢
- D ▢
- E ▢

3
- A ▢
- B ▢
- C ▢
- D ▢
- E ▢

4
- A ▢
- B ▢
- C ▢
- D ▢
- E ▢

5
- A ▢
- B ▢
- C ▢
- D ▢
- E ▢

6
- A ▢
- B ▢
- C ▢
- D ▢
- E ▢

7
- A ▢
- B ▢
- C ▢
- D ▢
- E ▢

8
- A ▢
- B ▢
- C ▢
- D ▢
- E ▢

9
- A ▢
- B ▢
- C ▢
- D ▢
- E ▢

10
- A ▢
- B ▢
- C ▢
- D ▢
- E ▢

11
- A ▢
- B ▢
- C ▢
- D ▢
- E ▢

12
- A ▢
- B ▢
- C ▢
- D ▢
- E ▢

Section 2

EXAMPLE
- A ▢
- B ▢
- C ▢
- D ▬
- E ▢

1
- A ▢
- B ▢
- C ▢
- D ▢
- E ▢

2
- A ▢
- B ▢
- C ▢
- D ▢
- E ▢

3
- A ▢
- B ▢
- C ▢
- D ▢
- E ▢

4
- A ▢
- B ▢
- C ▢
- D ▢
- E ▢

5
- A ▢
- B ▢
- C ▢
- D ▢
- E ▢

6
- A ▢
- B ▢
- C ▢
- D ▢
- E ▢

7
- A ▢
- B ▢
- C ▢
- D ▢
- E ▢

8
- A ▢
- B ▢
- C ▢
- D ▢
- E ▢

9
- A ▢
- B ▢
- C ▢
- D ▢
- E ▢

10
- A ▢
- B ▢
- C ▢
- D ▢
- E ▢

11
- A ▢
- B ▢
- C ▢
- D ▢
- E ▢

12
- A ▢
- B ▢
- C ▢
- D ▢
- E ▢

Section 3

EXAMPLE
- A ▢
- B ▬
- C ▢
- D ▢
- E ▢

1
- A ▢
- B ▢
- C ▢
- D ▢
- E ▢

2
- A ▢
- B ▢
- C ▢
- D ▢
- E ▢

3
- A ▢
- B ▢
- C ▢
- D ▢
- E ▢

4
- A ▢
- B ▢
- C ▢
- D ▢
- E ▢

5
- A ▢
- B ▢
- C ▢
- D ▢
- E ▢

6
- A ▢
- B ▢
- C ▢
- D ▢
- E ▢

7
- A ▢
- B ▢
- C ▢
- D ▢
- E ▢

8
- A ▢
- B ▢
- C ▢
- D ▢
- E ▢

9
- A ▢
- B ▢
- C ▢
- D ▢
- E ▢

10
- A ▢
- B ▢
- C ▢
- D ▢
- E ▢

11
- A ▢
- B ▢
- C ▢
- D ▢
- E ▢

12
- A ▢
- B ▢
- C ▢
- D ▢
- E ▢

Section 4

EXAMPLE
- A ▬
- B ▢
- C ▢
- D ▢
- E ▢

1
- A ▢
- B ▢
- C ▢
- D ▢
- E ▢

2
- A ▢
- B ▢
- C ▢
- D ▢
- E ▢

3
- A ▢
- B ▢
- C ▢
- D ▢
- E ▢

4
- A ▢
- B ▢
- C ▢
- D ▢
- E ▢

5
- A ▢
- B ▢
- C ▢
- D ▢
- E ▢

6
- A ▢
- B ▢
- C ▢
- D ▢
- E ▢

7
- A ▢
- B ▢
- C ▢
- D ▢
- E ▢

8
- A ▢
- B ▢
- C ▢
- D ▢
- E ▢

9
- A ▢
- B ▢
- C ▢
- D ▢
- E ▢

10
- A ▢
- B ▢
- C ▢
- D ▢
- E ▢

11
- A ▢
- B ▢
- C ▢
- D ▢
- E ▢

12
- A ▢
- B ▢
- C ▢
- D ▢
- E ▢

Section 1

EXAMPLE	1	2	3	4	5
A ▭ B ▭ C ▭ D ▭ E ▭	A ▭ B ▭ C ▭ D ▭ E ▭	A ▭ B ▭ C ▭ D ▭ E ▭	A ▭ B ▭ C ▭ D ▭ E ▭	A ▭ B ▭ C ▭ D ▭ E ▭	A ▭ B ▭ C ▭ D ▭ E ▭

6	7	8	9	10	11	12
A ▭ B ▭ C ▭ D ▭ E ▭	A ▭ B ▭ C ▭ D ▭ E ▭	A ▭ B ▭ C ▭ D ▭ E ▭	A ▭ B ▭ C ▭ D ▭ E ▭	A ▭ B ▭ C ▭ D ▭ E ▭	A ▭ B ▭ C ▭ D ▭ E ▭	A ▭ B ▭ C ▭ D ▭ E ▭

Section 2

EXAMPLE	1	2	3	4	5
A ▭ B ▭ C ▭ D ▭ E ▭	A ▭ B ▭ C ▭ D ▭ E ▭	A ▭ B ▭ C ▭ D ▭ E ▭	A ▭ B ▭ C ▭ D ▭ E ▭	A ▭ B ▭ C ▭ D ▭ E ▭	A ▭ B ▭ C ▭ D ▭ E ▭

6	7	8	9	10	11	12
A ▭ B ▭ C ▭ D ▭ E ▭	A ▭ B ▭ C ▭ D ▭ E ▭	A ▭ B ▭ C ▭ D ▭ E ▭	A ▭ B ▭ C ▭ D ▭ E ▭	A ▭ B ▭ C ▭ D ▭ E ▭	A ▭ B ▭ C ▭ D ▭ E ▭	A ▭ B ▭ C ▭ D ▭ E ▭

Section 3

EXAMPLE	1	2	3	4	5
A ▭ B ▭ C ▭ D ▭ E ▭	A ▭ B ▭ C ▭ D ▭ E ▭	A ▭ B ▭ C ▭ D ▭ E ▭	A ▭ B ▭ C ▭ D ▭ E ▭	A ▭ B ▭ C ▭ D ▭ E ▭	A ▭ B ▭ C ▭ D ▭ E ▭

6	7	8	9	10	11	12
A ▭ B ▭ C ▭ D ▭ E ▭	A ▭ B ▭ C ▭ D ▭ E ▭	A ▭ B ▭ C ▭ D ▭ E ▭	A ▭ B ▭ C ▭ D ▭ E ▭	A ▭ B ▭ C ▭ D ▭ E ▭	A ▭ B ▭ C ▭ D ▭ E ▭	A ▭ B ▭ C ▭ D ▭ E ▭

Section 4

EXAMPLE	1	2	3	4	5
A ▭ B ▭ C ▭ D ▭ E ▭	A ▭ B ▭ C ▭ D ▭ E ▭	A ▭ B ▭ C ▭ D ▭ E ▭	A ▭ B ▭ C ▭ D ▭ E ▭	A ▭ B ▭ C ▭ D ▭ E ▭	A ▭ B ▭ C ▭ D ▭ E ▭

6	7	8	9	10	11	12
A ▭ B ▭ C ▭ D ▭ E ▭	A ▭ B ▭ C ▭ D ▭ E ▭	A ▭ B ▭ C ▭ D ▭ E ▭	A ▭ B ▭ C ▭ D ▭ E ▭	A ▭ B ▭ C ▭ D ▭ E ▭	A ▭ B ▭ C ▭ D ▭ E ▭	A ▭ B ▭ C ▭ D ▭ E ▭

Section 1

EXAMPLE	1	2	3	4	5
A ▬	A ▭	A ▭	A ▭	A ▭	A ▭
B ▭	B ▭	B ▭	B ▭	B ▭	B ▭
C ▭	C ▭	C ▭	C ▭	C ▭	C ▭
D ▭	D ▭	D ▭	D ▭	D ▭	D ▭
E ▭	E ▭	E ▭	E ▭	E ▭	E ▭

6	7	8	9	10	11	12
A ▭	A ▭	A ▭	A ▭	A ▭	A ▭	A ▭
B ▭	B ▭	B ▭	B ▭	B ▭	B ▭	B ▭
C ▭	C ▭	C ▭	C ▭	C ▭	C ▭	C ▭
D ▭	D ▭	D ▭	D ▭	D ▭	D ▭	D ▭
E ▭	E ▭	E ▭	E ▭	E ▭	E ▭	E ▭

Section 2

EXAMPLE	1	2	3	4	5
A ▭	A ▭	A ▭	A ▭	A ▭	A ▭
B ▭	B ▭	B ▭	B ▭	B ▭	B ▭
C ▬	C ▭	C ▭	C ▭	C ▭	C ▭
D ▭	D ▭	D ▭	D ▭	D ▭	D ▭
E ▭	E ▭	E ▭	E ▭	E ▭	E ▭

6	7	8	9	10	11	12
A ▭	A ▭	A ▭	A ▭	A ▭	A ▭	A ▭
B ▭	B ▭	B ▭	B ▭	B ▭	B ▭	B ▭
C ▭	C ▭	C ▭	C ▭	C ▭	C ▭	C ▭
D ▭	D ▭	D ▭	D ▭	D ▭	D ▭	D ▭
E ▭	E ▭	E ▭	E ▭	E ▭	E ▭	E ▭

Section 3

EXAMPLE	1	2	3	4	5
A ▭	A ▭	A ▭	A ▭	A ▭	A ▭
B ▭	B ▭	B ▭	B ▭	B ▭	B ▭
C ▭	C ▭	C ▭	C ▭	C ▭	C ▭
D ▬	D ▭	D ▭	D ▭	D ▭	D ▭
E ▭	E ▭	E ▭	E ▭	E ▭	E ▭

6	7	8	9	10	11	12
A ▭	A ▭	A ▭	A ▭	A ▭	A ▭	A ▭
B ▭	B ▭	B ▭	B ▭	B ▭	B ▭	B ▭
C ▭	C ▭	C ▭	C ▭	C ▭	C ▭	C ▭
D ▭	D ▭	D ▭	D ▭	D ▭	D ▭	D ▭
E ▭	E ▭	E ▭	E ▭	E ▭	E ▭	E ▭

Section 4

EXAMPLE	1	2	3	4	5
A ▭	A ▭	A ▭	A ▭	A ▭	A ▭
B ▬	B ▭	B ▭	B ▭	B ▭	B ▭
C ▭	C ▭	C ▭	C ▭	C ▭	C ▭
D ▭	D ▭	D ▭	D ▭	D ▭	D ▭
E ▭	E ▭	E ▭	E ▭	E ▭	E ▭

6	7	8	9	10	11	12
A ▭	A ▭	A ▭	A ▭	A ▭	A ▭	A ▭
B ▭	B ▭	B ▭	B ▭	B ▭	B ▭	B ▭
C ▭	C ▭	C ▭	C ▭	C ▭	C ▭	C ▭
D ▭	D ▭	D ▭	D ▭	D ▭	D ▭	D ▭
E ▭	E ▭	E ▭	E ▭	E ▭	E ▭	E ▭

11+ Non-verbal Reasoning

Year 4/5

Testpack A
(GL Assessment Style)

Practice Papers 1-4

Answers and guidance notes for parents

These practice papers can be completed as standard or multiple-choice tests.

Multiple-choice Tests
Your child should mark their answers on the multiple-choice answer sheets. It is important for them to treat it like the real thing and record an answer in the appropriate box by drawing a clear line through their chosen box with a pencil. Clarity is important as the actual test would be marked by a computer. Mistakes should be carefully rubbed out and not crossed out since this would not be correctly recorded by the computer.

Marking and Feedback
The answers are provided in this booklet. Only these answers are allowed. One mark should be given for each correct answer. Do not deduct marks for wrong answers. Do not allow half marks or 'benefit of the doubt', as this might mask a child's need for extra help in the topic and does not replicate the real exam conditions. Always try to be positive and encouraging. Talk through any mistakes with your child and work out together how to arrive at the correct answer.

Timing
Each test should take 40 minutes, however it is more important that a child completes the test accurately and does not rush. Children will speed up naturally with practice.

Score	%	Score	%	Score	%	Score	%
1	2%	13	27%	25	52%	37	77%
2	4%	14	29%	26	54%	38	79%
3	6%	15	31%	27	56%	39	81%
4	8%	16	33%	28	58%	40	83%
5	10%	17	35%	29	60%	41	85%
6	13%	18	38%	30	63%	42	88%
7	15%	19	40%	31	65%	43	90%
8	17%	20	42%	32	67%	44	92%
9	19%	21	44%	33	69%	45	94%
10	21%	22	46%	34	71%	46	96%
11	23%	23	48%	35	73%	47	98%
12	25%	24	50%	36	75%	48	100%

Answers

Practice Paper 1

Section 1	Section 2	Section 3	Section 4
1) A	1) C	1) E	1) B
2) E	2) A	2) A	2) C
3) C	3) C	3) A	3) C
4) C	4) A	4) D	4) B
5) E	5) D	5) A	5) C
6) D	6) B	6) B	6) A
7) E	7) C	7) D	7) C
8) C	8) A	8) D	8) D
9) A	9) E	9) A	9) E
10) C	10) B	10) E	10) C
11) D	11) D	11) B	11) E
12) B	12) B	12) C	12) A

Practice Paper 2

Section 1	Section 2	Section 3	Section 4
1) B	1) C	1) D	1) B
2) E	2) B	2) B	2) D
3) C	3) C	3) E	3) B
4) A	4) E	4) A	4) E
5) D	5) A	5) A	5) C
6) B	6) D	6) C	6) D
7) C	7) B	7) E	7) B
8) A	8) D	8) C	8) E
9) E	9) B	9) E	9) B
10) D	10) E	10) B	10) A
11) A	11) A	11) E	11) E
12) D	12) C	12) D	12) C

2

Answers

Practice Paper 3

Section 1	Section 2	Section 3	Section 4
1) B	1) D	1) B	1) E
2) E	2) A	2) D	2) A
3) B	3) C	3) B	3) B
4) C	4) D	4) D	4) A
5) A	5) E	5) A	5) A
6) E	6) B	6) C	6) E
7) D	7) D	7) E	7) D
8) B	8) A	8) D	8) B
9) A	9) E	9) C	9) C
10) C	10) B	10) B	10) D
11) E	11) C	11) E	11) B
12) B	12) D	12) A	12) C

Practice Paper 4

Section 1	Section 2	Section 3	Section 4
1) C	1) E	1) C	1) D
2) D	2) A	2) D	2) B
3) A	3) B	3) C	3) E
4) D	4) A	4) E	4) C
5) E	5) E	5) C	5) B
6) C	6) A	6) B	6) D
7) A	7) D	7) E	7) A
8) D	8) C	8) B	8) C
9) B	9) D	9) A	9) E
10) B	10) D	10) B	10) E
11) C	11) B	11) A	11) A
12) D	12) C	12) E	12) C

PROGRESS CHARTS

Paper	Total Score	Percentage
Practice Paper 1	/ 48	%
Practice Paper 2	/ 48	%
Practice Paper 3	/ 48	%
Practice Paper 4	/ 48	%

Overall Percentage | **%** | For the average add up % and divide by 4

CERTIFICATE OF

ACHIEVEMENT

This certifies

_____

has successfully completed

11+ Non-verbal Reasoning
Year 4/5

TESTPACK **A** PAPERS **1-4**

**Overall percentage
score achieved** [   ] **%**

Comment _____

_____

Signed _____
(teacher/parent/guardian)

Date _____